By and By, I Reckon

By and By, I Reckon

Brenda O'Bannion

Tranquility Press 2020

For information:

Tranquility Press
723 W University Ave #300-234
Georgetown TX 78626
TranquilityPress.com
TranquilityPress@gmail.com

This is a work of creative nonfiction. While all the stories in this book are true in essence, some parts have been fictionalized to varying degrees to avoid hurting anyone or for literary purposes, and some names and identifying details have been changed to protect the privacy of the people involved.

ISBN: 978-1-950481-24-8
Library of Congress Control Number: 2020948380

Publisher's Cataloging-in-Publication data

Names: O'Bannion, Brenda, author.
Title: By and by i reckon / by Brenda O'Bannion.
Description: Georgetown, TX: Tranquility Press, 2020.
Identifiers: LCCN 2020948380 | ISBN (trade) 978-1-950481-24-8 | ISBN (e-Book) 978-1-950481-25-5
Subjects: Louisiana—Biography | Widows—Finance, Personal | Education—Study and teaching—United States | Families | Parent and child | Rural poor | Mentally ill children—Family relationships | Miscarriage—Psychological aspects | United States—Social life and customs—1918-1945
BISAC / Historical / General
Classification: LCC HC102.5A3-2 | DDC 330.9—dc23 | LCC HC107A.13 | LCC HQ2039.L8 | DDC 331.4—dc23 | LCC HQ801.A5-Z | LCC HQ755.85 | DDC 306.8—dc23 | LCC HQ773.8 | DDC 362.2—dc23

To the memory of

Granny and Dawfie.

We loved you and miss you.

Acknowledgements

Thank you to my family for holding on to the stories and seeing the value of passing them on. This story is bits of stories told to me and pieces I filled in from research until the time when I had my own memories. With prayer and middle of the night pondering, I've recreated my grandmother's life with as much care and respect as possible. It is my hope my family will accept it as a tribute to a life well lived and not dwell on the details.

Thank you, Dana, for being the baby in the front seat and not crowding the three of us riding in the back on our family road trips. Thank you, Charlotte, for helping me remember how our grandmother spelled.

And thank you, Mike, for all the research, listening, and encouragement as this story grew. You help me to be a better writer and a better person.

Part I
1917- 1924

I will instruct you and teach you in the way which you should go; I will counsel you and watch over you.
Psalm 32:8

Chapter One

As a child, I lived surrounded by family with little money and even fewer ways to earn it. The only people we knew were related to us, most of whom lived in similar economic circumstances. It might have bothered me more, but at the time, it was all I knew.

When my twin and I enrolled in a new school during our eighth-grade year, the secretary instructed us to choose between band and choir as an elective. Until this day, I'd been immune to the effect of living in poverty. My life never gave me a glimpse into a world where money made things possible. In this moment, I came face to face with a truth: in poverty there are no choices, only realities. Buying an instrument for band required funds; singing didn't. Choir became my reality.

Then came the next sting of poverty. All choir members were required to wear a black skirt, white blouse, and black shoes for the annual recital. My gut tightened when I heard this. Our wardrobe was as limited as the bills in Mama's purse.

Our mother managed to secure the mandatory black skirt and white blouse, but black shoes were a problem. My twin and I never had more than a single pair of shoes each school year. This year our shoes were cream-colored. Not to be defeated, we painstakingly colored each pair with black shoe polish. It took several coats of polish with at least a fifteen-minute drying time between applications. The results of this intense labor were passable black shoes.

It might have worked if it had not rained the night of the performance. As we stood on the riser, waiting for the curtain to go up, the shoe polish dripped into a black pool around our wet cream-colored shoes. Snickers from the choir erupted into laughter. When the choir director realized the reason for the commotion, she lashed out—not at the students for laughing, but at my twin and me for not having the correct color shoes.

I can't recall her words, but I do remember their sting. All the raging emotions of my thirteen-year-old body surfaced in a flash. The humiliation and embarrassment of the situation were nothing compared to the hot poker of seething anger in my gut. I now knew I was different. Standing on the riser, trying to sing my part, I resolved to someday have something better, which included a closet full of shoes.

At age thirteen, the resolve came from my first bitter taste of poverty. Years later, I realized it came from something much deeper. Listening at my grandmother's knees as she told the events of her life, I heard stories full of grit and resilience. This is the stuff running through my veins, as surely as the river runs at the end of the road where she lived her life.

Red dirt sprinkled with pine straw made the river road rock-hard in the dry season and muddy when the rain came. Carved through a pine forest, the tall, majestic pines lined the road like sentries saluting their leader. The road ended in a swamp which lay before the river which marks the boundary between Eastern Texas and Western Louisiana. My relatives relied on the road as the only way out of the river bottom. Their life on this road, like the river itself, flowed slowly. One day drifted into the next with little change. Even the seasons seemed to stall, melting into each other with only a subtle difference.

When my family lived on the river road, the land in this area belonged to the Boise-Cascade Lumber Company. Harvesting the virgin longleaf pine began in 1897, spanning from Virginia to Florida and eastern Texas.

The pine lumber industry grew at a rapid rate, providing economic growth. Most of the virgin longleaf pine forests were gone by the 1920s. To the lumber company's credit, they replanted the land with the loblolly pine, a faster growing and more prolific pine, albeit an ugly second cousin to the splendor of the longleaf pines whose towering heights were said to "tickle the angels' toes."

Boise-Cascade still owned the land after the initial harvest of the virgin pine, letting the loblolly grow to harvesting stage. My family leased small plots of land known simply as "Company Land" for one dollar a year. They never owned the land and depended on the timber company to keep the river road passable.

Longleaf pines rose tall on the left side of the river road. These majestic trees survived the clear-cutting practice of the lumber company and created a high wall around the family settlement. I loved them because of their beauty. The family loved them because "t'wert nobody's business how we live."

Having almost no cost of living other than building their small homes, none of the family had a need to leave the river road for long-term employment. They forged and hunted, living off what the river and the land had to offer. Their small gardens, chickens, and milk cow rounded out their needs. Supplies not forged or grown could be bought at the small store about half a mile down the road—or half the distance through the woods. When provisions were needed, the man of the family would cut wood for one of the many small outfits who sub-contracted with the lumber company.

The community of Bivens consisted of a store, a cemetery, and two churches. It barely had bragging rights to be called a community, but it did give the nearby residents a place to buy provisions, a place to worship, and a place to be buried.

The unpainted, one-room store sat close to the road. The small stoop extending from the front door had to have steps coming off each side rather than straight out. Inside it smelled of butchered meat and cow feed. The wooden floors echoed with each step. Cartons of milk and butter were placed in the meat cooler, which sat next to the soda container on the only wall with an electrical outlet. The root beer, orange drink, and ginger ale screamed out at us kids when we entered the store. We rarely had the cash to purchase the coveted sodas.

Sales were rung up on a large black register with numbers on small round keys and tabs that popped up the price inside a glass case each time the keys were pushed. Hitting the small black keys made a percussive sound like someone striking a drum.

Pushed against the cash register, a shoebox held the credit tablets. Every family had their own tablet where the store owner recorded sales until money became available. In my growing-up years, the store never changed, and it never failed to interest me.

Behind the store was the Church of Christ, a place of less interest to me although it played a huge part in Granny Leola's life. Like the store, the small church stood naked of paint. Behind it sat the necessary but ominous outhouse. An unfenced, well-cared-for cemetery resided beside the church.

Just north of the store, the Baptist church sat in a clearing hidden by pine trees. I never saw this church, not because it wasn't visible from the road, but because the family "don't hold with no Baptists."

My father left home at the age of 18. He never lived on the river road again, but he stayed in close connection by visiting often. As a young girl, I loved our trips to the river road.

Mama would announce mid-week the plan to go "check on Granny and Dawfie." Late on Friday afternoon, my family of six piled into the car. Daddy drove and Mama sat up front with baby sister. We three girls rode in the back seat. More accurately, we hopped from the seat to the space below the back window to the floorboard. This continued until Mama hollered, "Stop acting like heathens." She never explained what a heathen might be, but it always worked. Whatever the meaning, my sisters and I didn't want to be one.

At some point during the trip to the river road, Mama would fix fold-over wiener sandwiches, passing them around until we were full, or the supply ran out. I still love fold-over wiener sandwiches and continued the custom with my own kids. I called them "car picnics," code for "We're broke and can't stop at McDonald's."

If we didn't end up on the side of the road with an over-heated radiator or a flat tire, often the case when traveling, we crossed the Sabine River from Texas into Louisiana within about four hours. Then, six miles beyond the state line, we turned south on a county road. Twelve miles of winding, narrow road brought us to the river road.

Since our journey always started after our father got off work on Friday, we arrived late in the evening. Give out from trying to not act like heathens, we sisters often fell asleep in a sprawled heap in the back seat. Once there, Mama rustled us up. "Wake up, girls, we're here."

We were instantly awake, hustling to unwind our bodies and trying to find our shoes from the pile we'd thrown in the floorboard.

Our grandmother would come stand on the front porch as soon as she heard the car pull up into her yard. "Y'all get out and come in. Good to see ya, Son."

We'd "sit up" for several more hours as Granny Leola, a talented storyteller, told us the family news and eventually drifted into stories of the past. Gathered with the folks around the fireplace, I felt more than the warmth from the fire. I felt the warmth of belonging.

This is where I learned about life on the river road. The grit and resilience of my family were embedded in these stories, though at the time, I understood little of the deeper character of the stories. To me, the storytelling was about hearing my grandmother's deep-southern accent as she painted pictures with her words and I watched her go through the nightly ritual of unbraiding then re-braiding her long hair as she spoke. Later in my life, I'd realize how these family stories girded me up and carried me through tough times. My footprints remain deep in the red dirt of the river road.

Chapter Two

My family never made plans. Securing the future by planning in the present seemed as foreign as living in a house with a full staff of servants. We lived each day without thought for tomorrow. Sometimes a paycheck depended on the weather since my father worked in construction. Or there were no paychecks because he was out of work. It's difficult to plan for the future if cash flow is erratic. For this reason, in the spring of our senior year in high school, my twin and I had no plans for the future.

A few words from my English teacher change the road I would follow. While returning essays, she paused before handing out my paper and whispered, "You're an excellent writer. I think you should go to college and become a teacher."

My heart skipped several beats as I took in what just happened. *She likes my writing and she thinks I can teach! She sees me.* Then I realized she expected a response. I mumbled something profound. "Uh, okay."

Of all my teachers, this was a teacher whom I respected, partly because she taught the subject I liked, but mostly because she let us write. No longer naïve about the effects of poverty on my life, I knew living in poverty often meant being invisible to others. When I wrote, I could be anyone I wanted to be. I was no longer invisible.

The next 30 minutes of class crawled by as I processed the possibility of going to college. Thoughts spun around in my head like salad in a spinner. *Is it possible? Where would I go? What would my parents say? How would I pay for it?* By the end of class, a resolve rose within me. I would go and I would become a teacher—and maybe someday, I'd be a writer.

Armed with words of praise and a strong determination, I visited the counselor's office as soon as the class ended. I had two questions. "Can I go to college?" and "Can you help me find the money?"

With a student loan and a teaching grant, I was almost there, but I still needed my parents' signature on the loan. The night I told them of my plan was a long one, filled with frustration and determination. Their words, "People like us don't go to college" were met with my own, "Well, I do." Looking over to my twin, I added, "We do," even though I had not fully convinced her to come with me. The battle continued for the next few weeks, but eventually my parents signed the loan papers and my twin agreed to join me.

We arrived at college with one suitcase each filled with a few clothes and the savings from our summer job. If we ate all our meals in the cafeteria using a meal ticket and each spent no more than three dollars a week from our savings, I calculated we could make it through two semesters before needing to work again.

With difficult classes, a small amount of funds, and difficulty living in a culture so far removed from the one I knew, I often struggled with feelings of discouragement. *I don't fit in. This isn't possible. I'll never make it through.*

Then I'd think of my grandmother and her stories—stories drenched with resiliency like syrup flowing over a stack of pancakes. I'd recall my favorite story, the one about her own determination to become a teacher. My resolve always returned, and I gradually learned to live in my new surroundings.

Martha Leola Swilley was born in 1903. That same year the Wright brothers attempted to fly at Kitty Hawk, the Ford Motor Company was launched, the first World Series occurred in baseball, and Franklin Roosevelt became engaged to Eleanor. It's not likely Leola's parents knew much of these events, which were far removed from their life on a rural farm near a small East Texas town.

At the time of Leola's birth, almost half the population in the country lived on farms. Like them, her family lived off what the land provided, often making do or doing without. As the oldest child, Leola grew up doing the work of an adult. Younger children arrived in quick succession, requiring assistance from the eldest sibling. She learned early how to milk a cow, tend a garden, and stitch and mend clothing. Daily, Leola helped with the cooking, washing, and child rearing, and assisted her father with caring for the farm animals, hoeing and planting.

The garden, vital to their way of life, had priority during the growing season. From mid-summer into early fall, the table creaked under the bounty of fresh vegetables and fruits. Leola's day started as soon as the sun was up when she and the rest of her family fed the animals, ate a quick breakfast, and started their garden work. Gathering the ripe vegetables and going through the canning process put everything else on hold, her mother often commenting, "When the vegetables start comin' in, you got no choice but to be out there. Otherwise they'd just be 'a-wasting on the vine."

Hogs also held a high priority. The men trapped feral hogs then raised them for meat and lard or to be sold for cash. Leola preferred working in the garden over tending to the hogs. Again, her mother could be heard saying, "They don't look like much for the raisin' but they shore look good on the table!" Chickens were fried for a Sunday meal or thrown into a pot with dumplings. The eggs were used for food or to barter for staples.

Chores of this magnitude left little personal time. But when she found a few moments in her day, Leola read every book the teacher loaned her. A good student, she loved learning and rarely missed school unless her mother needed her at home for a special chore such as the yearly heavy cleaning of the house or helping to sew clothes for the family. The school year was short—too short for Leola—because children were needed at home for the harvest, and again for the planting season.

Like most rural children in the early 1900s, Leola attended a one-room school where one teacher wrestled to teach the different ages of her students. Before long, Leola's teacher began to use her as a helper.

"I finished my work early each day when my teacher put me to helping the younger kids with their lessons. I'd rather be reading, but teaching seemed easy for me and she needed help with all those students! Because I helped her, she let me take home books to read at night. We didn't have enough kerosene to do much night reading, but when the daylight was longer, I did enjoy those books."

At age 14, Leola finished school. Her rural education stopped after eighth grade. By this time, she had tutored students since her own primary grades. Prompted by her teacher, Leola began to focus on receiving her teaching certificate.

In the state of Texas in the early 1900s, completion through the eighth grade and passing a state teacher's exam allowed single women to teach in the rural schools. Since Leola couldn't take the exam until age 17, she and her teacher, Miss Kelly, hatched a plan. The next three years, Leola became an assistant while the teacher tutored her for the exam.

Deep in the Piney Woods of Texas, in a one-room

school, Leola received her teacher training with three years of hands-on experience from a busy teacher who scratched out short snips of time to tutor her.

When Leola turned seventeen, legal age to take the exam, her plans were put on hold. Traveling to the state capital required money for a train ticket. She also needed cash for room and board for the four-day exam. For Leola, money was hard to come by. Not spending her days at school, she used her sewing skills to make clothing for people in the community. She also saved her egg money from chickens her parents gave her.

Each day, Leola worked on her sewing. Every other day, she took her eggs to the store to sell. Winter offered Leola plenty of time to earn cash, but when planting and harvest time arrived, there was little time to earn money.

Even though the early 1920s experienced a period of huge economic growth, none of this prosperity impacted the community where Leola lived. Discouraged by how little money she was able to save, her dream began to feel hopeless.

By 1923, Leola was twenty years old—an age when society expected women to be married. The Great War created a time when there were more women of marrying age than there were eligible men, the result of which was women who faced a life without marriage. In the isolated area where Leola lived, finding a husband proved particularly difficult. With no suitors on the horizon, she appeared to be approaching spinsterhood. Concerned for her future, Leola's mother advised her to "get on a-teachin'" and rallied the relatives to help pay for the trip to Austin.

The idea of "marrying of the girls" didn't change much over our family's generations. When I started high school, my mother gave me similar advice: "Take home economics in case you get a husband and typing in case you don't." In the family's view, getting a husband hailed as paramount for survival. Training to do something other than marrying became a back-up plan.

With the help of her relatives, Leola secured enough funds to take her trip to Austin. Seven years after finishing the eighth grade, she traveled 250 miles from home and took the state teaching certificate exam. Traveling so far from home and attempting to take a state exam were two things no one in her family had ever done.

Chapter Three

After eighteen years of teaching, I moved into an administrative role which required traveling to Austin a couple of times a month.

Thoughts swirled in my head as I watched my speed, terrified of getting a speeding ticket in a state vehicle. *Can I find the meeting location? Will I be able to manage the traffic? What if I wreck this car? Will I be able to understand the round-table discussions with the other directors from around the state?*

I glanced down at the speedometer. It read fifty miles per hour. The speed limit on the highway into Austin was seventy. No wonder cars were passing me! I pulled over and sat in my car weeping.

What frightens me about this trip? The thought hit me: *I'm not worthy of this job.*

Memories of poverty popped in my head like popcorn kernels bursting open in hot oil, making me feel inadequate and different from my peers. Even years after pulling myself out of poverty, I still carried a "People like us don't..." mentality.

Like so many other times in my life, Granny came to mind. I remembered her stories about her trip to Austin in 1923. She, too, had been afraid of traveling far from home, alone, to a place she'd never been. Yet she found the grit to do it. I recalled every small event of the story she shared with me many times—a story filled with determination. My resolve grew. If Leola could make this trip, so could I.

Leola's ma moved around the kitchen quietly. Soft snores came from the rest of the kids who were still asleep. Ma's movements were jerky, her mouth set in a tight line. Finally, she spoke in a low voice. "Hits a long train ride, Leola. Reckon I'll fix you some ham and biscuits for the trip."

Pa came in from feeding the animals. "Ol' Lucy wouldn't be settlin' down to eat much. Think she knows she's goin' on a trip today." Leola smiled. The mule had always been her favorite farm animal. It would be a long workday for the faithful old animal. Leola would like to give Lucy a carrot as a treat when they arrived at the train station. But on the farm, vegetables were for humans, not animals.

After a whispered prayer in which Pa asked for traveling grace for his eldest child, the three ate a quick breakfast. Then Pa pushed back his chair. "Best be a-goin', sun's comin' up."

Leola grabbed the battered cardboard suitcase

loaned to her by a cousin. It had seen better days. Once a bright blue, it had faded through the years until the shade now resembled a pair of well-worn overalls. Mice had chewed a hole the size of a fifty-cent piece in the lid, seeking to build a nest.

With cardboard cut from an oatmeal carton, Leola fixed the hole. Then she glued a piece of brown paper over the patch and wrote her name and address. Leola checked the latches, glad they still worked. *It might not look like much, but it's better than carrying my clothes in a feed sack.*

Ma handed her daughter a brown bag containing the food. "Be careful in that big ole' city, Daughter."

Lucy nickered as Leola and Pa approached the wagon. After placing her suitcase in the back, she pulled herself into the seat next to Pa. He gave the mule a strong, "Git up there, Lucy," and they were underway.

Leola glanced back for a final look at the house. Ma stood on the front porch wiping tears away with the end of her apron. For a moment, Leola lost her resolve. She wanted to jump from the wagon and stay home. Then she remembered how hard she'd prepared for the test, the encouragement and help from her teacher, and the sacrifices made by her relatives and friends for her to make this trip. *I can't let myself or the others down.*

Determined to hold back her own tears, Leola studied the surrounding countryside, familiar to her as her own bedroom after these twenty years. May's beauty filled the landscape. Early morning sun glistened on the dewy grass. Wild pink azaleas, redbud trees, and white dogwood blooms filled the pine forest with a tapestry like one of Ma's quilts. Scents from the wild honeysuckle lingered on the air, giving it a mild sweetness she enjoyed breathing. She loved her home and looked forward to being back in a few days. Knowing she wouldn't be in her own bed come nightfall made her stomach tighten.

Holes and mud from the spring rains filled the road to Jasper, slowing the trip. Leola hoped they wouldn't be late. The train for Beaumont left at mid-morning. If she missed it, she wouldn't make her transfer from Beaumont to Austin.

As the sun rose higher in the sky, Lucy began to tire and slowed her pace even more. The last few miles to Jasper passed at a snail's pace. Leola checked her watch for the time. Pa surprised her with the watch a few nights ago. "Reckon you'll be needin' to know the time in that big city, Leola."

Ladies wristwatches had only been available in the last few years. Before this, any time device for them came in the form of a brooch to be pinned on the chest. Leola's heart swelled each time she peeked at the watch. She knew Pa used his tobacco money to purchase it.

By her calculations, they should make it to the station with enough time for her to buy a ticket and say goodbye to Pa. She spent the last mile recalling the many things Miss Kelly had explained to her about the trip.

Finally, they arrived at the train station. Pa jumped down and got the old suitcase from the back. Leola stepped from the wagon and looked around, her heart racing. When she saw the ticket window right where her teacher said it would be, her heartbeats slowed to an almost normal rate.

Pa handed her the suitcase. "Reckon are ya gonna be all right, Leola?"

"Y'sir, I reckon so." Leola tried to sound brave.

"A'right, then. I'll be here when you git back."

Pa climbed into the wagon and headed back in the direction they had come. She watched until the wagon went around a bend, knowing as soon as he got back home, Pa and Lucy would be in the garden for the rest of the day. Spring plowing wouldn't wait.

Leola turned and walked up to the window. She bought a ticket on the Kansas City Southern Railway from Jasper to Beaumont with money pinned in a deep pocket of her skirt. Ma had insisted on this, fearful the money would be lost or taken. "Now don't let that money out o' your sight, Leola. That's what'll git you home."

By the time she had her ticket, the whistle sounded, far off at first, then louder as the train got closer. She watched the train pull into the station. It was one of the railway's oldest trains, having made many round trips from Arkansas to southeast Texas. *Ol' Lucy might be more reliable than this rickety thing*. Leola took a deep breath and boarded. A long journey lay before her.

The scents of tobacco and old leather greeted Leola as she stepped on the train. The car, filled with mostly men, had trails of smoke curling above the heads of all the passengers. A seat in the back of the car next to an elderly woman remained empty. She made her way there quickly, sighing a breath of relief. *At least, I'll be out of some of the smoke.* She settled into her seat with a quick "hello" to the lady passenger. Then she glanced at the other passengers. Some were talking to each other; a few were reading newspapers. Leola felt better. *They don't seemed concern about this old train. Reckon it'll make it just fine.*

As soon as the train pulled from the station, the elderly lady seated next to Leola fell asleep. Relieved, Leola sat quietly for fear of waking her. She turned to the passing landscape. The tall pine trees slowly gave way to flat coastland. Fascinated with land she had never seen, Leola moved her head from left to right, peering out both sides of the moving train.

The train stopped at four small towns before reaching Beaumont, giving Leola a chance to see towns she'd known only by name. Excited each time the train slowed for another stop; she studied the buildings around the station. *I'll have a lot to talk about when I get back home.*

Three hours later, her train arrived in Beaumont. Getting off the train, she trembled at the thought of transferring to another train. This time, however, she had a better idea of what a ticket window looked like. Pushing aside her fear, she walked up to the window and purchased a ticket on the Southern Pacific Railroad for the trip to Austin. The ticket agent told her where to go to board the train.

These rail cars appeared newer. The larger windows and plusher seats promised a more comfortable ride on this part of the trip. By the time Leola found an open seat, she relaxed enough to feel the tension leaving her like flour falling from a sifter. As the train pulled out of the station, her growling stomach reminded her she hadn't eaten since before sunlight. Opening the brown bag, Leola blessed Ma for providing ham and biscuits. As she ate, she went over Miss Kelly's instructions for this trip.

"When you get to Austin, make sure to check the train schedule before leaving the station, so you know when your train is leaving for home. Then look for the streetcar which runs from the station to the University of Texas. This is where the test is given. Get off at the university and walk two blocks south on Guadalupe Street. The Bremond Boarding House for Young Ladies is on the same street. You'll see a sign out front, so you can't miss it. There, you'll be given a room to share with one of the other young ladies taking the test. Your breakfast and dinner will be served at the boarding house. You'll need to purchase your noon meal at the university.

"You need enough money for four nights at the boarding house because the test takes three days to administer. When the last test is over, you'll spend one more night before coming home. On the fifth day, catch the early streetcar to the train station. The train out of Austin will leave early, so don't miss it."

The thought of doing all this by herself made Leola almost lose the biscuits she'd eaten for lunch. Taking a deep breath, she tried to concentrate on the scenery out her window. Large, sprawling oaks dotted rolling green hills. Large ranches filled with cows and horses caught her attention. She'd never seen spreads as large as these.

The train went through several large metal trellises spanning wide rivers. Until now, she'd only read of these rivers in her geography books.

Leola watched with interest when the train stopped at the towns sprinkled along the railway line, seeing sights she'd never seen. At one stop, cars chugged by, passing the horse-drawn wagons with ease. In another town, a long train with the words Ringling Bros. and Barnum & Bailey Circus on the side of long boxcars sat on a parallel track.

Workers moved around like bees swirling a hive, each doing their job to load animals, equipment and circus entertainers. To Leola's delight, a couple of elephants lumbered up a ramp toward cavernous boxcar doors. Giggling, she wasn't sure the slow, monstrous animals would make it up the ramp before their train departed.

Then angry words broke into the scene. The two trainers held long whips over their heads, which they cracked on the rumps of the elephants while yelling for them to move forward.

Squeezing her eyes shut, Leola tried to memorize the scene, minus the whips, in the short time her train sat on the tracks waiting for passengers to board. *Won't it be something to share when I get back home!*

By mid-afternoon, the train pulled into Houston. Leola's jaw dropped when she saw the maze of trains and people, clearly the most massive gathering of people and things she'd ever seen. She continued to stare at the crowds until the train began to move slowly away from the busy station. *I'm glad I didn't have to change trains here.*

Before long, her thoughts returned to her

teacher's instructions, repeating them over and over in her mind. *I'm tired of all this thinking. I'm ready to start doing*.

The sun hung low in the western sky when the train approached the station in Austin. Leola sighed, relieved to finally be at her destination. She glanced out the train window as she stood and straightened her skirt, more familiar now with the sights and scenes of train stations. Pushing down her anxiety, she whispered to herself as she left the train. "I'll take it a step at a time. Can't be any harder than finding my way out of the woods behind our house."

Chapter Four

Leola's stomach flip-flopped as she stepped onto the platform at the station in Austin. The train had become her cocoon, a familiar place in an unfamiliar world. She took a moment to get her bearings.

Glancing around, the unusual sights became a blur. *How am I ever going to figure all this out? It looks like a swarm of bees.* Despite the hustle and bustle around her, Leola managed to find a trolley car next to the station. She rushed toward it, hoping it was the right one. Carrying her suitcase in one hand, she used the other to fish money from her pocket for the fare.

The trolley started moving the moment Leola entered the aisle. Panicked, she looked around for a place to sit. An empty place next to a gentleman reading a newspaper beckoned. But Leola hesitated. It took a mighty bold kind of female to sit down beside a man she didn't know, uninvited.

Suddenly the trolley made a quick left turn.

Teetering perilously, Leola grabbed the seat and eased herself into it. Better to sit next to a stranger than lose her balance and end up face down in the aisle.

A sharp jolt caused Leola to grab the side of the bench. Clinging to her suitcase she prayed, *Lord, don't let this wobbly contraption tip over!* Each time the trolley rolled over a track or made a turn, Leola's stomach lurched.

She surveyed the other passengers. *Are they as frightened as me?* The man next to her seemed lost in a newspaper. Two ladies across the aisle spoke quietly, talking about the purchases they held in their lap. Leola glanced over her shoulder to find the other passengers weren't paying any attention to the trolley movements either. *It must be safe, but I'd sure rather be behind Lucy in Pa's wagon.*

More at ease, Leola stared out the windows. Her eyes popped wide at the scenes before her. People crowded the sidewalks, some strolling, others walking with purpose. Stores lined both sides of the street. There were ice cream parlors, barbershops, dress shops, millinery shops, markets, and even a shop for buying tobacco. Leola checked her watch. A wave of homesickness washed over her. *I wonder what Pa would think of this ride?*

Thoughts of home ended when the driver announced, "Guadalupe Street." She grabbed her suitcase and exited the trolley car with other passengers. After only a few steps, Leola came to a sudden halt, gasping in awe.

In front of her, a large brick sign stated The

University of Texas. Behind the sign, tall brick buildings were clustered around a tree-filled plaza. Leola set down her suitcase and stared.

I'd sure like to be a student here. Shaking herself out of her daydream, she picked up her suitcase. "Time to find the boarding house." Leola scanned the busy street in both directions, trying to remember what to do next. The words of Miss Kelly came back to her.

"When you get to the university, Leola, walk two blocks south on Guadalupe Street. You'll find the boarding house on the last corner." Leola squinted at the amber-red glow of the sun setting behind the row of storefronts, then turned left. As sunlight slowly gave in to the coming darkness, Leola began the last part of her day-long journey.

"It surely feels good to be traveling on my own two feet again." Soon, Leola found herself standing in front of a large two-story house. Struggling to read in the fading light, she could just make out the sign hanging on white picket fence. ***The Bremond House for Young Ladies.*** Leola sighed and whispered, "Thank you, Lord, for getting me to the end of my journey."

With trembling knees, she walked onto the front porch. Two gas lanterns put a soft glow around the front door. *Should I knock or just go on in?* Then she spotted a doorbell. It had a small knob which triggered a spring causing a lever to hit against a bell. Leola had seen pictures of ringers in the Montgomery Ward catalog, but she'd never used one. Suppressing a giggle, she tentatively turned the knob once, then a second time with more confidence. She jumped at the loud clanking from the bell.

Leola waited. No one came. She reached out to ring the bell again when the large door flew open. A portly woman wearing a long dress made of cotton fabric covered with brightly colored flowers and finished off with yards of lace smiled at Leola. Several long strings of pearls hung loose around her neck. A bun on top of her head tilted precariously to the right.

Leola stood speechless, unable to pull her eyes away from the clothing. Then, she saw the lady's beautiful smile. *She's got a smile just like Ma's. Makes a soul feel better.* Leola's knees stopped trembling and she managed to smile back.

"You must be Leola. I'm Etta Bremond. We were getting worried about you. You're the last one to arrive. Well, come on in. We don't need any more mosquitos sneaking through the door."

Miss Bremond's swift speech made her words melt together like pats of butter in a sizzling skillet. Confused, Leola had no response.

"Come in, dear, don't be shy. We're having our evening meal. Just put your suitcase by the door and join us. We'll get you settled in later."

Leola snapped into action, hurrying through the door. She hesitated before placing her luggage on the floor. The tattered suitcase had been her only companion, her only link with home. Tenderly, she placed it on the floor of the entryway and followed her hostess.

In the dining room, several young ladies sat around a large table eating. Laughter and smiles erupted as if they'd known each other since childhood. Miss Bremond clapped a few times and the noise stopped. All eyes turned to look at Leola. She gave a wobbly smile, feeling like her feet had taken root in the glossy wood floor.

"Ladies, this is Leola, the last of the test-takers. She's come a long way and can probably use a good meal. Amelia, you and Leola will be roommates. Her place is next to you."

One of the ladies smiled and pointed to the empty chair next to her. "Have a seat, Leola. I'm glad to be sharing a room with you. Don't worry, I'm quieter than all these other clacking hens."

Leola willed her feet to move, taking the seat next to Amelia. Keeping her eyes down, she scanned the table covered in white linen and china as fine as anything she had ever seen. *This is something!* She looked up quickly, hoping she hadn't spoken out loud.

But the chatter had returned, picking up right where the ladies left it. Leola lifted her fork and began eating, grateful to have the attention off her. She ate slowly, sneaking a glance at one girl, then the next. *I'm glad Ma made my new dresses from store bought material instead of flour sacks. Never seen such fancy clothes except in catalogs.*

When the meal finished, Miss Bremond took Leola aside. "Now, Leola. You've already met your roommate, Amelia. For the next four days, breakfast and dinner are provided. You'll need to get your own lunch while on the university campus. Do you understand?"

"Yes'm. My teacher explained everything to me."

Miss Bremond continued. The more she said, the faster she talked. "I won't collect the room and board fee until the night before you leave. Some girls don't make it through the test before giving up and heading home." Her hostess stared hard at Leola, sizing her up. "You don't look like a quitter, so I expect you'll be here through Friday."

Leola tried to focus on her hostess's long list of instructions. *Her lips move faster than a hummingbird's wings.* "...my fee is four dollars a night." Leola heard this clearly, her breath catching in her lungs as she realized the enormity of the statement. The Bremond House for Young Ladies had increased its fees.

Leola calculated her bill for four nights at the new rate. *I don't have the funds to cover everything.* Heartsick, Leola forced her attention back to Miss Bremond.

"Now, I'll let you go upstairs to unpack. Your room is at the top of the stairs, second door on the right. Breakfast is a 7:00 a.m. Have a good night, Leola."

Too confused and embarrassed to share her problem, Leola mumbled good night to her hostess and turned to go up the stairs. Each step echoed her one thought: *What am I going to do?*

Chapter Five

At the top of the stairs, Leola stopped and put her suitcase on the floor. Taking a deep breath, she straightened her skirt. "There must be some way to solve this problem," Leola whispered, her voice trembling and her eyes blinking back tears

Standing alone in the hallway, Leola thought of Ma. She'd heard the story Ma's journey by wagon from Mississippi to Texas as a young wife many times. Now the tale came alive, giving her a shred of hope.

...It was a hard trip, Leola. There be swollen rivers to cross, wild animals to watch out fer, broken wheels to fix, and hungry mouths to feed. I learnt to face each day's problems and let God carry me through.

Leola whispered a quick prayer. *Lord, carry me through this*. Then, she picked up her suitcase and turned toward the room. After a timid knock on the door, she heard Amelia's voice. "Come on in, Leola".

Leola opened the door into a room large enough

to hold two beds with small bedside tables, a large wardrobe, and two small desks. Gas lamps affixed to the wall gave the room a soft glow. A muted-colored woven rug covered the wood floor. Pretty pink floral curtains hung from a large window, under which sat a window seat complete with a long blue cushion and several embroidered pillows. A large, white wicker rocker sat in one corner next to a small round table draped with lace-edged beige fabric. Kerosene lamps with a colorful globe sat on the bedside tables. For a moment, she stood, her mouth hanging open.

Amelia smiled. "Pretty, isn't it? Miss Bertrand makes every room in the house nice. She says girls should be surrounded by fancy things. Better not get to use to it. I doubt we'll see this kind of fancy wherever we board once we're teachers. But for now, let's just enjoy our time here."

"I reckon I could get used to this, although I feel like a chicken in a flock of peacocks." Leola opened her suitcase on the bed nearest the window and began to unpack. She listened to Amelia's non-stop jabbering, trying to make appropriate responses.

Her roommate chattered about her home in San Antonio. Soon, she moved on to talk about the other girls, where they came from, where they wanted to teach and so on. Switching gears, she spoke of an older brother who had attended the University of Texas. "I know exactly where the testing room is on the campus. I can get us there in the morning."

Leola found it hard to concentrate on her roommate's gibbering. Her mind only had room for her problem. *I hate to not be friendly, but I really need to think. If I don't find a way to make this work, I'll be headed for home tomorrow.*

Relieved when Amelia went to the hallway bathroom to prepare for bed, Leola moved to the window seat. Moonlight flooded through the curtains, casting a soft glow on her skin.

A wave of homesickness washed over her. *I sure wish I could talk to Pa. He'd know what I should do.*

A memory came flooding back of another night when a full moon poured its light into her small room keeping her awake. On that night, she heard Pa whispering to her ma in the next room.

"Hit's lookin' like the crop is gonna be poorly. I'm thinkin' I might be needing to hire on a lumber crew for a spell. We'll be needin' some cash for food this winter."

Ma's voice wavered. "But, Henry, this here baby's due in just a few weeks and I don't know if I can manage everything."

"They're needing men now for the last harvest of lumber before winter sets in. The older kids can help you. I'll only stay until I get enough money for us to make it until we have crops again."

He paused for a long moment, then continued in his low, croaky voice. "I reckon the way we make it in this life is to grab opportunities when we know about 'em."

Leola closed her eyes. "God, I need an opportunity. I'd be obliged if You'd show me one before morning."

Amelia came back to the room. "Bathroom's free now, Leola, if you're needing it."

Glad for the opportunity to clean some of the

travel grime off before bed, Leola slipped out of the bedroom. When she returned, the soft sounds of sleep came from Amelia. *She probably gave up trying to talk to me. I hope she doesn't think I'm not friendly.*

Leola crawled into the big bed, the softness of the sheets and the warmth of the beautiful handmade quilt hugging her like an old friend. A breeze fluttered the curtains, causing moonlight to dance over her bed. Her body, tense from the long trip and the new surroundings, finally began to relax. But her mind continued whirling, flitting from one thought to the next. *There's no way to stretch my already tight funds to cover the cost of four nights here. Either I find a way to make this work, or I head home on the morning train.*

Then she remembered something Miss Beasley had told her.

Leola, the test is in several sections. All the test-takers must complete each section before anyone can start the next. It slows the process down some, but it also gives you plenty of time to check your answers. Use the time wisely, Leola, and you'll do fine.

Leola sat up in bed. An idea took shape in her mind. *What if I could take the next part of the test without waiting on the others? Surely it would move me along faster and I could finish the test in three days instead of four.*

Her mind churned as she thought about the possibility of asking for this special favor. *God, could this be my opportunity?* She wrestled with the idea until the early hours of the morning. Exhausted, she fell into a fitful sleep.

Chapter Six

My principal, Mr. Willett, called two days before the start of school. "I need to change your assignment to fifth grade for this year." Panicked words tumbled from his mouth. "The Texas Education Agency called me this morning. They said our fifth graders must pass their state test this year or they're coming to visit. My job is on the line!"

The in-coming fifth grade class of eighteen students had a reputation. Every student failed their state exam in the third and fourth grades. One of the students explained it this way: "We're the dumb class." Under pressure, the principal had only one assignment for me: "Make sure they pass."

I made a plan of action and implemented it with the determination of a general taking his troops into battle. Every day we worked hard, cramming learning into every minute. Most days the students embraced the challenge. Some days they rebelled, justifying their behavior with whinny phrases. "It's too hard; there's too much to do; this is stupid."

A few weeks after taking the exam, a knock on my classroom door interrupted a difficult math lesson. I opened the door to find my principal—beaming brighter than the overhead fluorescent lights.

"I'll tell you what, you've taught these kids from bell to bell and you haven't let anybody interrupt you, not even me." He waved test results in my face. "Well, it worked."

With teary eyes, Mr. Willett looked at the class, his voice breaking. "You did it! You all passed your test."

Silence engulfed the room as the students absorbed the news. Then a loud celebration broke out. "We did it! We beat that ole' test! We're not the dumb class anymore!" One of my students expressed our happiness best when he shouted, "Eww, whee! We in high cotton now, ain't we?"

"Better get up, sleepyhead. Breakfast is in thirty minutes," Amelia said as she slipped out the door and headed downstairs.

Sitting up, it took Leola a few moments to realize she wasn't at the farm. Then the memory of the previous evening rushed into mind. For a moment, she considered packing her suitcase and hurrying to catch the early train home.

No, the train left at seven a.m. Too late to make it today.

Leola gazed at herself in the mirror after pinning

up her braids. "Well, I guess I'll go and ask about my idea. If they say no, I'll head home tomorrow."

As Leola descended the stairs, her resolve faded. Maybe she could confide in Amelia about her problem. But no; Pa always said, "Don't reckon it be anybody's business about my family or my money." As his daughter, she'd never ask for pity or for help.

After breakfast, Leola fell in step with the other girls as they walked the two blocks to the university.

Amelia moved to the front of the group. "Come on, girls, I know exactly where we need to go. Just follow me."

Glad Amelia didn't expect them to walk together, Leola fell to the back of the group. She needed time to collect her thoughts.

Far sooner than she wished, they were on the large tree-filled campus. Leola looked around. *This place must be larger than my hometown and the next town combined!*

Amelia efficiently led the little group to the testing building, pointing to the different buildings on the way. "There's the cafeteria. It's close to where we're taking our test."

In the testing room, Leola found herself in line with the other girls, waiting to register for the exam. Breathing deeply, she surveyed the room. The odor of paper, lead, wood and pencil shavings filled her nose. *Like my classroom back home.*

Maybe the scent reminded her of her old school, but nothing else did. The large, rectangle room appeared different in every way from the classroom where she'd spent most of her youth. This room had a high ceiling and shiny wood floors. Big white globes hung from the ceiling casting a yellow glow around the room. Tall windows lined one long wall and a large chalkboard attached to another wall designated the front of the classroom. Under the chalkboards, two long tables were piled high with stacks of testing papers. Rows of small tables faced the chalkboard each with three chairs facing the front of the room, waiting for occupants. Several of the chairs were already filled.

Two men in suits stood near the stacks of tests. The short, portly man seemed to be giving instructions to the other one, who remained silent while giving nods of understanding.

They must be the proctors. That's who I should talk to. Stepping out of line, Leola made her way across the large room.

She held back for a moment, her heart pounding loud enough to drown out the conversations in the room. Then she took a deep breath and stepped closer to the man who seemed to be in charge.

"Sir, may I speak with you, please?"

The short man turned, thrust out his chest and stared at Leola. "Excuse me, Miss, we're having an important conversation about administering this test. What is the reason for this interruption?" Glaring over the top of his glasses, his manner demanded a response.

Leola fought to find her voice, praying her knees wouldn't buckle under the harshness of this man. "I'd be beholden if you'd let me take the test in three days instead of four. If I don't have to wait for everyone to finish each section, I think I can complete it early. I don't have enough..."

Before she could explain the reason for her request, the man shook his head several times. Leola stopped in mid-sentence, wondering what to do next.

The other man cleared his throat, catching Leola's attention. With kind eyes and a soft voice, he said, "Young lady, I suspect this is a matter of finances. Am I correct?"

Leola nodded, hoping he'd ask no more about her problem.

"And if you pass this exam, do you plan to teach in a rural part of our state?"

Surprised by the man's second question, Leola stammered. "Y'sir. I reckon I'll be teaching as close to my home as possible." She continued, explaining where she lived in East Texas.

"Then I say yes to your request. It's far too difficult to find teachers for our rural schools. If you think you can manage it, we'll administer the test to you separately, allowing you to move at your own speed."

"It's preposterous. We can't..." The short man snorted, again puffing out his chest. Leola waited for his vest buttons to go flying across the room.

"Yes, we can, and we should. We're desperate to get teachers to the rural schools in our state. We're a large state and it's a hardship to travel to Austin to take this test. If this young lady wants to try this, I see no reason to hold her back."

He leveled a hard stare at Leola. "Given, of course, you keep your agreement and teach in rural schools only."

"Y'sir. You've got my word on it."

"Good, it's settled. You'll be allowed to move at your own pace, not waiting on others. After you register, take the small table near the window where we can change out the test sections without disturbing the other test-takers. Of course, we ask you not to discuss the test with anyone else at the end of the day, since you'll likely be well ahead of the rest."

Leola's lungs breathed normally for the first time since the night before. "I'm thanking you for your understanding. And I know folks back home thank you too. I won't be sharing anything about the test."

She hurried back to where Amelia stood in line. "I'll be taking my test at the small table near the window." Amelia opened her mouth, but Leola quickly added, "I'll talk to you at lunch." She could feel Amelia's eyes on her back as she walked to the end of the registration line.

Sitting at the small table near the window, Leola looked around. *I like it here by the window. There's natural light, not the yellow light from those big globes. And a cool breeze.* She took her pencils out of her bag and a small pocketknife for sharpening. *Can't waste time going to the crank sharpener. Or waiting in line.*

After giving instructions about testing procedure, the proctors distributed the first section of the test. Leola glanced down the first page, then put her head down and began answering questions as carefully and quickly as possible. When she finished, she raised her hand, hoping the tall, kind man would bring her the next section.

She groaned inwardly when she saw the short proctor headed toward her. He placed the test section on the table while picking up the one she had finished. Standing in front of her, he reviewed her work – his lips folded together in a tight line. "Humph," he whispered.

Each time she needed another section, the same proctor brought it over to her. By noon, his face had lost some of its sternness, though he still studied Leola's work before leaving her table.

Leola met Amelia just outside the testing room when they were released for lunch.

"Why in the world are you rushing through the test? Don't you want to use the time to review your answers?" Leola knew others in the room had the same question.

"I have to leave for home on Friday, so I must finish the test on Thursday." She reached in her pocket for some change. "I need to make a call home right now. I'll meet you in the cafeteria." Leola turned and headed to the phone booth at the end of the hallway. She knew Amelia wanted more of an explanation. *God, please let her understand and not ask too many questions.*

At the booth, she quickly dialed the general store back home, asking the storekeeper to get a message to her family. "Please have my pa meet the train in Jasper on Friday instead of Saturday. Tell him I'm fine and I'll explain when I get home."

Hanging the phone back on the hook, Leola sighed. Exhausted from the tension of the morning, she longed to sit under the shade of one of the large oaks surrounding the plaza and rest her eyes—but she needed to eat. *I'll need the strength for the rest of the test today.* She exited the testing building and turned in the direction of the cafeteria.

For the next two days, Leola took the test at her little table near the window. By now, the proctor acted pleasant each time he brought her the next section. The girls from the boarding respected her silence and didn't push for answers.

When she turned in the last of her test on Thursday afternoon, the short proctor finally smiled. "Well, Miss Swilley, I don't know if you passed, but I applaud your grit in getting the test finished early."

Leola thanked him and slipped out of the room, following the other test-takers. She walked behind the others, lost in her thoughts. *It's over. I just hope I passed.*

On Friday morning, Leola said her good-byes to Miss Bremond and the other ladies. She hugged Amelia on the sidewalk then watched as the group headed toward campus. Finally, she turned toward the trolley stop. *I've done what I came to do. Time to get on home.*

Taking the four-day test in three days may prove to be a mistake. Still, she knew the folks back home would support her whether she passed or failed. If she passed, they'd celebrate, proud of one of their own. If she failed, they'd probably blame it on "those government people."

Chapter Seven

As a girl, I made many long trips with my family to see my grandmother in old cars which had seen better days. One trip turned the four-hour journey back home into a long ordeal. Shortly after leaving Granny Leola's house, the temperature gauge in our car read as hot. My dad pulled over, raised the hood, and mumbled a string of words we couldn't hear but knew the meaning of. The radiator had a hole, causing it to lose water rapidly.

With no funds to stop at a repair shop, Dad filled the leaking tank with water from hoses found at gas stations. If we pulled into a station with no outside water spigot, we drove around town looking for another station, leaving a trail of smoke billowing from the front of our car. Somehow, we'd find a place with water and continue our trip.

Each time we were underway again, my sisters and I watched the little needle on the temperature gauge. Slowly it moved back into the green area. Before many miles passed, the needle crawled through the amber and back into the red. Swinging our eyes from the gauge to the front of the car, we looked for the tell-tale smoke billowing from the hood. Then our eyes would begin searching for a place with water.

When we were between towns, Dad pulled the car over beside ditches filled with rainwater. Using the only container he had—his cap—he crawled down to the ditch. After filling his cap with water, he carefully walked out the ditch, trying not to spill any of the precious water. It took many trips to the ditch before he got the radiator filled to the top. By the time Dad got back in the car, sweat and frustration poured from his body.

Tired of crawling in and out of ditches, the next time the gauge read hot, he pulled over and gave all of us a stick of gum. "Chew it a little then give it back," he instructed. He mixed the chewed gum with some mud, making a plaster. Then, he pushed the concoction in and around the hole in the radiator. This time the water stayed in the tank.

Seven hours later, we finally made it home thanks Dad's cap, chewing gum, and our spit.

Leola arrived at the trolley stop as the car began to roll away. She jumped aboard and found an empty bench, breathless from her hurried approach. As the rickety car made its way down the middle of the street, Leola scanned both sides of the trolley, trying to absorb all the sights. An early morning fog covered the buildings like a thin white shawl. It had been a wonderful adventure. Still, her heart yearned for home.

When the trolley came to a stop at the train station, Leola glanced around in surprise. She saw nothing resembling the quiet place she had arrived at a few days earlier. Then there were only a few passengers disembarking from the train and even fewer waiting to board. Now, a large crowd of passengers waited to board the next train out of Austin.

Leola joined a long line of people at the ticket window. She finally made her way to the front of the line just as the train approached the station. After purchasing her ticket, Leola hurried to the platform where she stood shoulder-to-shoulder with other passengers. *Goodness, I feel like a pickle stuffed into a pickle jar.*

As soon as the train came to a stop, the crowd lunged forward. Leola moved with the other passengers, struggling to hold on to her suitcase. Within moments she boarded a car, frantically searching for a seat.

She took the first open spot on the benches and sat down with a gasp. She had just settled her suitcase under the bench when a tap on her shoulder made her look up.

"Excuse me, Miss. I believe this is yours."

Leola's hand flew to her head where, sure enough, she found no hat. She stared at the man, stunned by his beautiful blue eyes and by his smooth, deep voice. For a moment she couldn't move. Finally, she grabbed her hat from the stranger. Plunking it on her lap, she cast her eyes down and mumbled a quiet "Thank you."

"Have a pleasant trip, Miss."

Leola nodded without raising her head. When the gentleman moved on, she let out the breath she'd been holding. *My goodness, why couldn't I talk? He's just a man—but I admit a very nice-looking man.* She giggled. *Guess I'm not so different from the girls at the boardinghouse. I'll not be sharing this part of my trip with anyone.*

Leola's car overflowed with passengers who sat elbow-to-elbow on the narrow seats. Across the aisle, a mother with three young boys and a baby girl struggled to settle the children and get all their belongings stowed beneath the bench.

The train lurched forward. The two youngest kids began to whine, and the baby let out a loud cry while the oldest boy held the bench with white knuckles. The mother pressed her hand over trembling lips.

"You know," Leola spoke softly to the oldest boy, "I was scared the first time I rode a train. But soon it settled into a soft rocking just like being in a cradle. Imagine that—someone as old as us being rocked!"

The boy released his grip on his seat and gave her slight smile. Exhaling, the mother turned to Leola. "Thank you. This is our first trip on a train. My husband is working in the oil fields around Beaumont. We're joining him there. Getting the kids and our belongings there is overwhelming."

"Well, the worst is over now. You can sit back and enjoy the scenery. We'll see some pretty sights and cross several rivers before we get to Beaumont."

A smile slowly worked its way across the mother's face as her eyes filled with tears. "I guess you're right.

All there is to do now is sit here and wait until we reach the other end where my husband will be waiting for us." She turned her attention to her children. "Y'all hear the nice lady? She said all we need to do is enjoy the ride. Let's watch out the window and see what we can find."

Leola turned back to her own window, watching the rolling hills go by. *When I see pine trees out this window, I'll know I'm home.*

Soon dark clouds moved over the hills. Within a few miles, heavy rain blocked the passing landscape. Bold lightening flashed through the rain, followed by a loud clap of thunder.

The two younger children and the baby across the aisle began to cry again. The oldest boy blinked rapidly, trying not to add more tears to the group.

They needed a distraction. Leola asked, "How would y'all like to hear a story about a farmer and a bunch of crows?"

Without waiting for a reply, Leola began the story, drawing the attention of the scared children.

Once, there came a rain just like this one. Only it lasted several days, making the river swell and run over its bank. The rain came in the late summer when the cornfields were ripe with lush ears of corn. The cornfields closest to the rivers were flooded right up to the tip of the corn stalks, making it impossible for the farmers to harvest the corn. Worse than that, the crows who lived nearby couldn't enjoy the corn they'd waited for all summer.

Now, a certain farmer stood on high ground looking at his cornfield. It lay farther away from the river and only had river water about knee-deep. Still, he couldn't get in the water to harvest the corn.

"Don't know what to do," the famer said. "By the time the river goes down, my corn will be hard, no good for eating. I reckon we won't be harvesting a corn crop this year."

He turned to leave the field when he saw two crows sitting on his scarecrow. "Humph, some good that scarecrow does." He waived his hands to scare off the crows when he heard one of them say something.

"Wait a minute, farmer," the biggest crow called out. "Maybe we can help."

The farmer stood stone still, not believing what he just heard.

Sighing, the big crow tried again. "Yes, we can talk when we need to. Just don't need to very often. But this is an emergency. There's hardly any decent corn in this whole county, except for yours. How about if we help you harvest the ears above the water?"

The second crow, smaller and a bit scraggly, spoke up. "Yeah, how about if we kinda work out a deal. You know, you help us, and we'll help you."

The farmer, desperate to save his crop, replied, "Okay, what's your plan?"

The two crows flew down from the scarecrow and landed next to the farmer. "We can pull the ears that are above the water and fly them to the bushel baskets in your wagon waiting on high ground. For every four bushels of corn, you give us one bushel. We'll have corn for the winter, and you'll get most of your crop."

"Weeell," the farmer scratched his beard, "it might

work, but how can two little ole' crows pick this whole field?"

"Oh, there's lots more of us. We'll go round them up. Is it a deal?"

The farmer smiled widely. "Deal!"

"Good. We'll go find the rest of the gang and be back soon. You go get your wagon and bushel baskets. Let's go, Bruce. Sun's already high and we've plenty to do."

"Wait a minute, Sam. I've one more thing to say." He turned to face the farmer. "Please take away your silly scarecrow. It ain't nothing but a roosting place and it kinda hurts our dignity, ya know?"

"Don't worry, it'll be gone before you get back. And thanks, thanks a heap!"

"No problem." Sam flapped his wings, eager to get started. "If it works out, maybe we can do the same thing next year, even if there's no flood. Might be a good thing for everyone."

"And that's what happened," Leola finished the story. "The crows helped the farmer with the harvest and came back to help every year at harvest time. Just goes to show you, when everyone lends a hand, there's not much that can't get done. Like all you kids helpin' your mama get through this train ride."

Leola reached in her suitcase and pulled out paper and pencils. "Now, y'all sit here real quite like, and draw a picture about this story."

"Thank you," the mother mouthed, careful not to wake up the baby who finally slept in her arms.

Leola nodded. *Maybe I'll be a good teacher after all—if I passed the test.*

Before long, the children fell asleep, sprawled over their mama and each other. The rest of the trip passed slowly, giving Leola time to reflect on the past week. *I'll remember this trip all my life.*

The rain continued as the train pulled into the depot in Beaumont. Leola helped the mother maneuver the kids, now awake and whiney again, off the train. As soon as they saw their pa, they brightened and rushed to him.

The mother turned to Leola. "Thanks again. Don't know how I'd have made it without you. You're a real blessing."

"You're welcome. I love kids and yours are sweet, just a little scared. They seem fine now." Glancing over, she saw them crowding against their pa, each trying to gain his attention first.

"Yes, but they can be a handful sometimes." She studied Leola for a moment. "You know, you'd make a great teacher."

"Thank you. Lord willing, it might happen someday." She smiled as the mother left to join her husband.

Leola found the correct platform to board the train to Jasper, relieved to see fewer passengers waiting for her train. Once onboard, she took a seat, happy to be on the last leg of her trip.

A few hours later, the rain stopped, and the late afternoon sun shone on the glistening needles on the tall pines. Leola smiled. *I'm home. Feels like I've been away much longer than a few days.* As the train pulled into the depot, Leola grabbed her suitcase, eager to be the first off. When she stepped onto the platform, she saw Pa standing beside the wagon.

"Well, you're home, Leola. Reckon I'm glad."

"Reckon I'm glad too, Pa."

She knew Pa wouldn't question her about why she came home a day early. He'd wait until she chose to tell her story. And she would, maybe over the evening meal. But now, Leola wanted to ride in the wagon and smell the sweet scents of wet pine trees and honeysuckle blossoms.

Chapter Eight

After moving to a new city, I left home early one morning with a stack of resumes to deliver to the school districts in the area. I hoped to secure a teaching job when school started in the fall.

Fifteen miles from the city, a small district lay nestled near a beautiful large lake. Considered a choice place to live, it didn't often have teacher openings. Still, I decided to stop since the next district lay thirty miles away, a longer commute than I wanted.

I handed my resume to a secretary, explaining what my certifications were, including special education. After thanking her, I headed out the door.

Suddenly, a loud voice boomed through the front office. "Don't let the lady leave!"

I stepped back through the open door. "Am I the lady?" I asked the secretary.

Before she could answer, a large man came running through a side door, adjusting his tie with one hand and holding a rumpled set of papers in the other. He came straight at me in a huff.

"You're hired," he said breathlessly, sticking out his hand for a shake.

"Hired?" Dumbfounded, I managed to return the handshake before continuing. "You haven't read my resume. And I haven't interviewed."

"Doesn't matter. I was on my knees asking God for a special education teacher and you walked in. God answered my prayer. The job is yours." A huge grin spread across his face, his eyes bright with tears.

My mouth hung open while I struggled with what to say next. Finally, I stammered, "But how can you hire me? You don't even know me."

"I'm the superintendent of this district and as such I have hiring privileges. Here's the contract and new teacher orientation packet. Just sign right here."

What could I do? God told him to hire me. I signed the contract.

After her trip to Austin, Leola's days were once again busy with farm life. She rose early, helped Pa with the animals, then worked in the garden most of the day. She spent her evenings "talkin' about the city" as her younger siblings called it. They'd settle on the front porch after supper to catch the night breezes while Leola told them about the things she'd seen and done, even what she ate. They loved her story about the elephants with the circus. "Tell us 'bout those big ole' elephants again, Sister."

Every Saturday, Leola walked the half-mile to the store to check the mail and get whatever supplies Ma might need. She tried not to be disappointed when she saw no letter for her. *I'd sure like to know if I'm a teacher or not. But, like Ma always says, "What will be, will be."*

Summer moved forward with relentless heat and enough rain to ensure a good crop but not enough to give concern about the river rising. One day in mid-July, Leola worked in the cornfield helping Pa pull ears from the stalks when she heard the voice of Mrs. Monroe, their neighbor.

"Leola, get over here. I got a letter for you. 'Hits from the Texas State Board of Education." Mrs. Monroe hurried her way across the pasture, waving a letter in her hand.

Leola dropped two ears of corn into the bushel basket and headed toward her neighbor. They met at the fence which enclosed the cornfield.

The neighbor could barely catch her breath. "I went to the store to pick up my mail and the postman asked me to bring this letter to you. He said he 'spected you might want to see it right away. You reckon 'hits telling you you're a teacher now?"

Leola took the letter in trembling hands. She stared at the front of the envelope.

"Don't think the letter's gonna open itself, Leola." Pa had walked over to the fence. "No use putting off any news, good or bad."

Leola opened the envelope with great care, not wanting to tear anything inside. A one-page letter lay inside. She pulled it out and carefully opened it. She only read as far as "Congratulations" when she turned to Pa with a huge smile. "Glory be, Pa. I passed. I'm a teacher."

Pa's face told Leola how pleased he felt. "Reckon you're in high cotton now, daughter."

Leola spent the next several evenings writing letters of introduction to school board presidents in the area. On Saturday, she walked to the store and mailed the letters with a quick prayer. *Father, I'm thanking You for helping me pass my test. Now I'm asking for a teaching job.*

Again, Leola waited for a letter—one offering her an interview for a teaching position. After a few weeks, she became concerned.

"It's getting late in the summer, Ma," Leola said one day while they were canning beans in the hot kitchen. "I may not get a teaching job. Maybe Miss Kelly will let me help out again for this year."

Ma never moved her eyes from the jar she was filling with snap beans. "Jest give God a chance, Leola. He'll provide."

Leola didn't correct her ma, although she couldn't imagine a job coming her way this late in the summer.

When evening came, Leola struggled to sleep. *I want to believe like Ma does. But I don't see a job for me this year. I have to accept that I may not be teaching when school starts.* When Leola finally fell asleep, she dreamed of a classroom full of kids

Temperatures rose even higher as the week

moved forward. Ma and Leola shelled the last of the pinto beans in the shade of the porch, which offered some relief from the sweltering heat.

"I'm thinking I'll go see Miss Kelly later this afternoon about helping her out again this school year." Not surprised when Ma didn't reply, Leola started again, hoping to draw Ma into a conversation. Before she could say another word, she heard a voice.

"Hello, I'm searching for Leola Swilley." A man stood outside the front gate. He removed his hat to fan himself. Perspiration clung to him like dew on morning grass. "Am I at the right place?"

Leola's heart hammered a beat as she handed her bowl to Ma and rose from her rocker. "I'm Leola Swilley. Please come on over."

The man opened the front gate and stepped onto the porch. "I'm James Lewis, president of the Stringtown School Board. I'd like to offer you a teaching job. School starts in two weeks and we'll need you there a few days early to get settled. The pay is $32.50 a month, including room and board. We usually interview before offering a position, but the board liked your letter of introduction and gave me the authority to hire you. I brought the contract and I'd be obliged if you'd sign it now." He swallowed hard as if he weren't used to such a long speech.

Leola fought for words. She turned to Ma. "What should I do?"

Ma offered one of her few smiles. "I thinkin' you need to say yes, Leola. Ain't hit what we prayed for?"

Chapter Nine

The moment Mr. Lewis stepped off the front porch, Ma flew into action. "Daughter, stop a'standing there starin'. We got plenty to do. I'm figurin' you'll need at least two more teaching dresses. No tellin' how often you'll be able to do your wash. We'll take my egg money into town tomorrow and buy fabric. If we sew every night, I'm thinkin' we can get 'em finished before you leave."

Leola stared at Ma. There would be no talking her mother out of this plan, but she hated for Ma to spend her savings. The egg money represented the family's emergency fund for doctor's bills, new shoes for the younger kids' growing feet, or replacing a broken farm implement. Best to go along with Ma's plan. "Yes'm, Ma. I surely appreciate it."

The next ten days were busier than Leola ever recalled. The warm temperatures of late summer meant vegetables were still producing. Leola worked alongside

Ma shelling, dicing, and canning vegetables all day. In the evenings, she cooked and cleaned up the supper meal so Ma could sew. Long after the rest of the family slept in their beds, she and Ma sewed the new teaching dresses. It became a bittersweet time for Leola. *When might I ever be doing this again with Ma?*

Now, the evening before her departure, Leola pulled the old suitcase from the top of her chifferobe. *It's still hard to believe I have a teaching job. Even harder knowing I'm leaving home.* The butterflies in her stomach began fluttering again, as they had been doing off and on for the past ten days.

How fast these last days at home have passed! Thank goodness for Ma's steady determination to get everything ready. I've been too excited and nervous to think straight.

Now, one of her new dresses hung on a wall peg, ready to put on in the morning. The rest of her clothes lay carefully folded in the old, faded suitcase along with her bible, a few of her favorite books, and some writing paper.

She crawled into her small bed for the last time. *Lord, I believe You sent this job to me. Now, help me be up to the task*. She fell asleep wondering how Ma would manage the chores without her help.

"Leola, Ma says it's time to get up." Her fourteen-year-old sister shook her shoulder gently.

"Oh my, did I sleep past breakfast?" Leola swung her feet to the floor.

"No, but Ma says you'll be needin' to hurry. Pa's already hitchin' up Lucy."

Leola rushed to change. She smoothed her skirt and glanced around the room. She'd miss this small retreat where she'd spent so many happy evenings reading and studying.

When Leola entered the kitchen, Ma put the bowl of scrambled eggs on the table, then turned to gaze at her daughter, as did every one of her siblings.

"Wow, Sister," her younger brother blurted out. "You look just like a school marm."

Leola glanced around at her family. Her eyes filled with tears. *How can I leave them?*

"You kids git to the table. Your sister has a long ride ahead of her." Ma turned to the stove, wiping an imaginary stain from the old black cookstove.

"Breakfast smells wonderful, Ma," Leola said in a shaky voice. "I reckon the meals I'll get at the boarding house won't be nearly as good as yours."

"Humph!" Ma replied, turning back to face the family.

Leola spotted Pa as he came in the front door and headed into his bedroom. She gave a questioning look to Ma.

"Your pa aims to dress decent when he delivers the new teacher," Ma said as she placed a big platter of fried pork sausages on the table.

Leola's heart thudded against her chest. *How can I leave them?*

Pa emerged from the bedroom and took his place at the table, ignoring the stares of the rest of the family. "Let's pray and get this meal over. Sister and I have plenty of miles to cover."

All too soon, everyone gathered on the front porch to say good-bye to Leola.

She hugged each of her siblings. "You kids be good. You older ones help Ma get the rest of the garden in." Turning to Ma, she grabbed her in a quick embrace. "I'll be thinking about you each time I wear one of these new dresses."

"You just be thinking about your students. Make us proud. Reckon that's enough thankin' for me." One of Ma's hands gripped the edge of her apron as she shooed her daughter off the porch with the other hand. "Go on now, Pa's a'waitin'."

Once the wagon started rolling away, Leola turned to wave a final goodbye. Ma's hands covered her heart. Tears worked their way from the back of Leola's eyes, threatening to spill down her cheeks. She bit her bottom lip, careful not to let Pa see.

"Growin' up is as natural as takin' your next breath, Leola. Reckon' we'll all be just fine with this change," Pa said as he kept his eyes on the mule's rear end.

Leola offered a weak smile. "Seems most of the change is on me. I can't help but worry about how y'all will make out."

The dew barely wore off the grass before the blistering heat of August beat down. Pa took off his hat and wiped sweat from his brow with his old handkerchief. "Reckon hit's hotter than a blacksmith's forge today."

Leola smiled. Pa never said much but when he did, his speech always held great description. *I hope I can teach my students to write with the same kind of flair.* Even with little talk between them, she savored this time with Pa. *Much as my sewing time with Ma.* The smoldering sun sat directly overhead when Lucy picked up her pace, seeming to know they had arrived at their destination. Leola stared at the old mule. *There's someone else I'll be missing.*

Stringtown appeared to be bustling despite the oppressive heat. Wagons, buggies, and horses filled the main street. A large mercantile store and a white clapboard church sat across from each other. A few homes dotted the street. Mr. Lewis told her the house where she would board sat near the school. *But where's the school?* Pa's slight tug on the reins brought her out of her musing. He'd pulled up in front of a small café.

"Don't want to be deliverin' the new teacher with a growlin' stomach. Reckon we'll see what they're servin' today."

How many more surprises will this day hold? Pa in his Sunday best and now taking me for a store-bought meal. Her heart swelled with love.

Thirty minutes later, their stomachs filled with meatloaf and boiled potatoes, Pa retrieved his suit jacket from the back of his chair. "I'll pay at the counter and see if the lady there can give us directions to the schoolhouse, Daughter."

In the wagon again, Pa headed farther down the

street where they found the small two-room school standing at the end of the street. To the left, a white two-story house sat just off the road. Pa slowed the wagon to a stop in front of it. The house had a large porch with inviting rockers. Several potted plants hung from the eaves. A white picket fence surrounded a dirt yard, recently swept clean. Leola and Pa stared at what would be her new home.

"Well," Leola broke the silence. "I guess I'd best make myself known, so you can head on back." She got out of the wagon and waited for Pa.

Pa laid his reins across the buckboard and jumped from his seat. He grabbed the suitcase from the back, then laid his hand on Leola's back. "Let's go on in, Leola."

Leola used the iron knocker. Soon the door opened and a petite, gray-haired lady with a smile as wide as Texas waved them in.

"You must be Leola. We've been expecting you. I'm Mrs. Crawford. The other new teacher is over at the school, working in her classroom. She'll be back for dinner. The town was plenty upset when we lost both our teachers in the same year. We feel so blessed to have found two replacements. Let's take a seat in the parlor."

Leola was instantly comfortable with Mrs. Crawford. She loved her soft-spoken voice and how her smile never left her face. Soon, she and Pa were sitting on a small parlor couch, listening to Mrs. Crawford's description of the town, the people and even the school kids.

Leola suppressed a giggle seeing her pa, hat in

hand, trying to sit comfortably on the fancy couch. *I'm sure he'd rather be sitting behind Lucy in the wagon.*

She turned to Mrs. Crawford, "Thank you for such a nice welcome. I know I'll be happy living here. If you might show me my room, I'll say good-bye to my pa. He has a long ride home."

"Of course. Just follow me. There are two bedrooms upstairs. You'll have one of those. I made the downstairs office into my bedroom after Willy passed on to glory. Never did care for climbing these stairs. Then the school board gave me the opportunity to start boarding our teachers. I have to say, I really enjoy the company. It's been lonesome without my Willy." Mrs. Crawford continued talking as she led the way up the stairs with Leola following. Pa came behind them carrying the suitcase.

"Here's your room, Leola. I'll leave you to say your good-byes now. Supper is at six." She started down the stairs, then turned back. "Oh, a few of the school board members will be by tonight to welcome you and discuss their expectations before school starts. You and the other teacher can meet with them in the parlor. I made my famous oatmeal cookies just for the occasion. Goodness me, here I stand running my mouth, when your father needs to be on his way." She hurried down the stairs.

"Don't think you'll be lonesome here, Daughter. That woman could talk the rattle off a rattlesnake." Pa grinned as he put her suitcase down and glanced around. "Reckon this will do you just fine."

Leola took a sharp breath as she gazed around

the lovely room. A colorful quilt in a Churn Dash pattern spread across the bed. The large, braided rug in several colors covered most of the floor. Beside the bed sat a chest with a mirror above it and a small rocker. The walls were papered with lovely tiny pink roses. In the dormer, an oak desk with a table lamp faced the window. She imagined herself grading papers there in the soft glow of the lamp. Smiling, she turned back to Pa. "I never imagined I'd have this kind of room."

Pa edged toward the door. "I'll be tellin' your ma you're in a right nice place. Reckon that'll make her happy, but you'd best be a-writin' her soon. She's gonna want every detail and she'll not be pleased with my memory of this place."

"Yes, Pa."

"All right, then. I'm a-goin' now. Be rememberin' to read your bible, Daughter."

"Yes, Pa." Leola couldn't find more words, though her heart had plenty to say.

Pa headed down the stairs with more speed than he'd come up. Leola moved to the window to watch him climb into the wagon. Pa peered up and gave a tip of his hat before turning the wagon to head home.

Leola watched him out of sight, then faced the room. She sat in the rocking chair, thoughts of the past week tumbling around in her head, her fast heartbeat matching the rapid movement of the rocker. Finally, the heartbeats slowed and so did the rocking. She remembered Pa's words, "Growin' up is as natural as breathing."

All right, Pa. I reckon I'm ready to grow up.

Chapter Ten

A quick rap on the door startled Leola awake. She jumped from the rocker checking her wristwatch. *5:50 already! Could I really have napped for so long?* She smoothed her dress and checked her hair before opening the door.

A small, thin woman a few years older than Leola stood in the doorway, arms crossed tightly over her midsection. She wore a plain brown dress and sturdy black shoes. A tight bun at the nape of her neck added to the sternness of her face. She frowned at Leola, squinting over her wire-rimmed glasses.

"I'm Wilma Griggs, the other teacher. I've taught for several years so I know the ropes. I'll answer your questions, but I'll only tell you once. I've enough to do with my own students without trying to train a new teacher. I'm sure Mrs. Crawford told you about a few school board members coming here tonight. No doubt to give us our copy of the Texas Rules for Teachers. As if there's anything we could do to break rules in this one-horse town." She glanced at her watch. "Supper's in ten minutes." Wilma turned and entered her own room, letting the door shut with a sharp bang.

Leola blinked. Her hopes of a good relationship with the other teacher burst in the slam of the door. *Lord, help me know how to befriend this teacher—and remind me to not ask too many questions.* She hurried to wash her face, then headed down the stairs.

The tedious meal seemed to drag on forever with Mrs. Crawford chattering nonstop. Wilma kept silent while Leola interjected comments in the mist of her host's continuous talk. Exhausted, she looked at her fellow teacher several times, but Wilma kept her head down while silently eating her meal. Irritation built up in Leola like tenders catching hold in a new fire. *Seems like she could make more of an effort to join the conversation.*

Eating meatloaf and boiled potatoes for the second time today, she thought of the meal she'd shared with Pa. Though the food seemed filling, it proved not as tasty as those prepared by Ma.

When the meal finished, Leola offered to help Mrs. Crawford with the dishes. She waited for Wilma to do the same, surprised when the teacher left the dining room without a word and headed up the stairs.

"Oh, no, it's a chore that's mine to do. You rest in the parlor. I'm sure the school board members will be here soon. Please answer the door when they arrive. I may have my hands in sudsy water by then." She smiled at Leola as she began to clear the table.

Leola made her way to the parlor, smiling when

she saw the sofa. How funny Pa looked sitting there. A pang of homesickness hit her in the gut and made her eyes water. "Breathe, Leola. Just one more piece of being grown up," she whispered.

Before she could sit down, the door knocker announced the arrival of the school board members. Leola hurried to the door, wondering if Wilma would come back down.

Wilma arrived at the end of the stairs just as Leola reached the door. "I'll do the talking, Leola. We can't let them think they can boss us around."

Not sure what she meant, Leola stepped aside and let Wilma open the door. After a flurry of introductions, the group soon found themselves sitting in the parlor, eying each other.

Mr. Lewis finally broke the silence. "As the school board president, I'd like to officially welcome you to our town. We want you both to feel..."

"Yes, well, let's get on with the business for this evening." Mr. Graves, who'd identified himself as the board treasurer, interrupted. "We're here tonight to officially give you ladies a copy of the Texas Rules for Teachers. Get to know them well, ladies. Breaking these rules could end your teaching job here, and maybe everywhere in the state." He handed Leola and Wilma each a piece of paper. "Please read this before school starts on Monday. And, of course, we all expect to see you both in church every Sunday."

Leola mumbled a quick "Thank you."

Wilma, her back straight as a rod, stared hard at Mr. Graves. "I'm sure we'll respect these rules, Mr.

Graves. I hope we can expect the same respect from the board."

Not sure how to respond, Mr. Graves grabbed his hat. "Well, we're done here tonight. My wife is waiting with dessert." He nodded to Mr. Lewis. "Ready, Calvin?"

Mr. Lewis nodded good-bye to Leola and Wilma and followed Mr. Graves out the front door.

Leola peered at her paper, curious to study its contents. After grabbing a couple of Mrs. Crawford's famous oatmeal cookies, she followed Wilma up the stairs. As before, the other woman entered her room with another loud slam of the door.

"I'm thinking you don't much care for these rules," she whispered to Wilma's closed door.

After getting ready for bed, Leola opened the window over her desk. A cool breeze made the curtains flutter as she pulled the lamp closer to her paper.

Texas Rules for Teachers, 1923

1. *Not to get married. The contract becomes null and void immediately if the teacher marries.*
2. *Not to keep company with men.*
3. *To be at home between the hours of 8 o'clock p.m. and 6 o'clock a.m. unless in attendance at school functions.*
4. *Not to loiter in downtown ice-cream stores.*
5. *Not to leave town at any time without the permission of the Chairman of the Board of Trustees.*
6. *No cigarettes or tobacco. The contract becomes null and void immediately if the teacher is found smoking or chewing.*
7. *Not to drink beer, wine, or whiskey. The*

contract becomes null and void immediately if the teach is found indulging in any alcoholic drink.

8. Not to ride in a carriage or automobile with any man except her father or brother.

9. Not to dress in bright colors.

10. Not to dye her hair.

11. To wear at least two petticoats.

12. Not to wear dresses more than two inches above the ankle.

13. To keep the schoolroom clean.

14. To sweep the classroom floor at least once daily.

15. To scrub the classroom floor with hot water and soap at least once weekly.

16. To clean the blackboard at least once daily.

17. To start the fire at 7:00 o'clock a.m. so the room will be warm at 8:00 o'clock a.m. when the children arrive.

Well, I'm glad I packed two petticoats. Leola turned out the light and crawled into bed. It had been a long, emotional day. *Tomorrow I'll work in my classroom. Maybe it'll cheer me up a little.*

After a fitful sleep, Leola woke up with a nagging headache. Her gaze spanned the unfamiliar surroundings. Homesickness made another unwelcome visit. *Lord, let this be a better day. Let me be thankful for all You've given me and not miss home too much.*

She dressed in an old work dress and grabbed a bibbed apron. *I'll go to the school right after breakfast.* The thought of seeing her classroom put a bounce in her step. She hurried through the door, almost missing a small piece of paper laying on the hallway floor just outside her bedroom. Curious, she bent to retrieve it.

Miss Swilley,

As a beginning teacher, you'll be expected to start the fire each morning and to do the weekly scrubbing of the classroom floors.

Wilma Greggs

"Well, I never!" Leola stuffed the note in her pocket and slammed her door, causing a loud bang. "We'll just see about that!"

Chapter Eleven

Leola set out for school determined to not let the crumpled note in her pocket spoil the excitement of seeing her new classroom.

Within minutes, she stood facing two doors spaced just a few feet apart on the front of the schoolhouse. One classroom served the first through fourth grade students. The fifth through eighth grade students were in the other classroom.

I don't think Wilma would take kindly to me going into her classroom. She might think I wanted to snoop. Glancing around, she spotted a water bucket beside the well in front of the school. Grabbing the bucket, Leola placed it under the closest window then put one foot on the bucket leaving her other foot dangling in the air. Through the window she saw a clean classroom ready for the first day of school, the small desks indicated it belonged to the younger students. When she turned to step down the bucket tipped, sprawling her to the ground.

Stunned, Leola lay in the dirt. Then she heard a loud chuckling from the edge of the woods. She sat up to see a man standing nearby. Dressed in a pair of overalls which had seen better days and heavy well-worn boots, he had a shabby hat pulled low over his forehead. A rifle lay hooked over one arm and a hunting dog waited at his side. As quickly as he appeared, he disappeared into the thick grove of pine trees.

"Well, that's plenty rude!" Embarrassed, Leola stood up quickly and glanced around, hoping no one else had seen her fall. Luckily, no other eyes witnessed her tumble.

She brushed the dirt off her skirt and entered her classroom door. There it was—her own classroom. The airless room smelled stale and musty from being shut up over the summer. Cobwebs outlined the ceiling and dust covered the desks scattered around the room. Forgetting the fall, her heart swelled. "My own classroom! Thank you, Lord."

Stepping farther into the room, she surveyed the students' desks and the teacher's desk. Books of all sizes and subjects were stacked haphazardly on a long bench near the door. Above the bench, a row of pegs provided a place for winter coats and hats.

A blackboard hung on the wall behind the table. Chalk residue and dust had turned it to a muddled gray. "I'll start with the board," Leola mumbled, eager to see the shiny blackboard where she would instruct her students.

First, she opened the front and side windows,

allowing a breeze to waft into the classroom. Leola returned outside to fill the water bucket. She couldn't resist a peek toward the woods. "Hope that man is long gone!"

Finding some cleaning rags in classroom closet, she set about bringing the blackboard back to life. Returning to the well twice to get fresh water, she persisted in cleaning the board until it gleamed.

Next, she turned her attention to the wood stove standing against the solid wall near the front door. "That'll need a good cleaning, but I'll wait until the weather turns cooler." She moved on cleaning the desks, and finally the wooden floor.

Satisfied with the clean room, Leola set out to arrange the desks. She placed the small desks up front near the chalkboard, then the larger desks near the wood stove. Four hours later, she stood in the doorway, surveying her work.

A low rumble in her stomach reminded Leola she hadn't eaten anything since breakfast. She took the sandwich wrapped in wax paper she'd made before leaving the boarding house and sat on the steps outside her room. Lost in thought about preparing her first lessons, Leola had almost finished her lunch when a large, lanky dog with short hair the color of mahogany appeared in her face.

"Woof." The dog stared at her sandwich.

"Hello, there. Where did you come from?"

"Woof!"

"I don't think I know where that is. Maybe a bite of this will make you more talkative." She pinched off a piece of the ham and extended it to the dog.

"Stop!" The man from the woods stood on the dirt pathway. "Don't you know no better'n to feed a huntin' dog? You'll ruin 'er for sure!"

Both feet planted squarely on the ground, he gave a sharp whistle and commanded, "Queenie, come!" He clearly expected his dog to obey.

Leola watched as the dog turned to her master, then back to the sandwich.

"Queenie, come!" the man bellowed.

The dog raced to him, and he turned and left without another word, the dog trotting by his side.

Leola jumped to her feet and watch the man out of sight, fists held tight by her side. Anger coursed through her veins. "Well, I never. That's twice today the same person has been rude to me!"

Gradually she released her fists released from tight balls. "Ma always says to allow everyone a bad day. I reckon this must be his."

Returning to her classroom, Leola determined to put him out of her mind and focus on preparing for her first days of teaching. She spent the next several hours perusing through the students' books and writing lesson plans. Gratefulness welled up in her chest for all Miss Kelly had taught her during her apprenticeship.

Soft colors of the late afternoon sun streamed through the window and danced across Leola's desk when she heard footsteps stomping up the outside steps. She'd given no thought about being alone with the door open. Glancing up, Leola gasped. The man from the woods filled her doorway.

"Miss, I'm sorry I laughed when you fell off that thar bucket. And I'm sorry I yelled at you 'bout my huntin' dog. Be askin' you to forgive me." He tipped his hat and headed down the path taking long, determined strides. Queenie followed close on his heels.

Leola sat with her mouth hanging open. *My goodness, I guess his day improved.* She put her hands to her cheeks, which grew hot at the memory of his eyes—deep hazel eyes with gold flecks. Eyes which portrayed a softness that contradicted the hardness his body presented.

Pushing her thoughts aside, Leola determinedly continued to work until the sun cast too little light to see her plans. As she prepared to leave, she glanced around the classroom. "It's still stark. Maybe I can make some curtains for the windows and ask Mrs. Crawford if she has a few potted plants to share."

Leola woke early on Sunday morning. While fixing her hair, she talked to her reflection. "I'm eager to visit a new church. I hope the people there are as friendly as Mrs. Crawford."

Then she asked herself, "I wonder if the man from the woods will be there?" The vision of him standing in her classroom door had returned several times the night before.

Leola met Wilma as they headed down for breakfast. "Would you like to walk with me to church, Wilma?"

"You'd best go on without me. I'll wait as long as

possible before I arrive. The school board can make me go, but they can't dictate the time I get there."

Leola hardly knew what to say. *Does Wilma have something against church, or is it authority she doesn't like?* She had no time to think about it any longer since Mrs. Crawford sat at the table chattering like a magpie.

"I'm excited to have you young ladies in church today. I know you'll love it. We just built it last year. Before then we used one of the classrooms at the school. It's so nice to have a real church building." Without taking a break, she continued. "Our pastor brings wonderful messages. And the singing, well, I'll just say it might be the best this side of heaven."

Leola glanced over to see Wilma roll her eyes. She suppressed a giggle. *Wilma might be hard to understand, but at least she's entertaining.*

Church lived up to Mrs. Crawford's promises. Tears began to build in Leola's eyes when the congregation sang *Sweet By and By*, her mother's favorite. The pastor delivered a thought-provoking message from Isaiah 41:10: *Fear not for I am with you. Be not dismayed. For I am the Lord your God. I am with you. Yea, I will hold you with the right hand of my righteousness.*

Leola went alone to the boarding house after church. Mrs. Crawford had lingered to visit, and Wilma was nowhere in sight, having apparently left the church as soon as the service was over. As she walked, Leola thought about the morning's scripture. *I have nothing to fear about my first day tomorrow. God's holding my hand.*

Chapter Twelve

The first day of school rarely changed except for the age of the student. Regardless of the grade, students arrived with shiny sneakers and new backpacks filled supplies, expectation evident in their faces. One first day, however, stands out in my mind as unusual.

I greeted my new students as they entered the classroom. Speaking to each of the parents as they arrived, I asked them to help their children find the desk with their name. This year, one parent didn't follow my request. Instead she charged directly at me, engulfing me in fog of perfume.

She took another step even closer, giving me a stare so hot it could've melted an iceberg. "When I pick my son up at the end of the day, I expect you to tell me if you think he'll be valedictorian of his graduating class."

Stunned at the parent's demand for me to predict her six-year-old son's academic future, I fell silent. Finally, I managed to speak. "What if we get him though the first grade and see where he is at the end of the year?"

Stepping back, the parent mulled over my response. Thankfully, she turned to help her son find his desk without another word.

I watched the pair as they walked over to the assigned desk. My heart squeezed with mixed emotions. Sadness for the little boy who probably had much pressure to perform and dread for me. *Will I meet this parent's expectation?*

A full moon filled Leola's room with enough light to see the papers on her desk. Unable to sleep, she'd been staring at them for the past few hours.

Am I prepared? Will my students like me? Will they behave? Not until the moon began its decent in the early hours of the morning did Leola finally fall asleep, only to dream of oversleeping on her first day of school.

The neighbor's rooster startled her from her sleep. Large, even by rooster standards, the pesky bird liked to perch on the fence outside Leola's window. She often watched him while working at her desk, admiring his bright plumage and impressive stance. *Oh, Barney. What a noisy rooster you are! But thanks to you, I should be on time for school.*

Leola dressed carefully, taking extra time with her hair and being sure to put on both her petticoats. Too early for breakfast, she spent time reviewing the names of her students and checking lesson plans.

An hour later, she gathered her plans. Checking

her hair once more, she spoke to her reflection in the mirror, a habit she hoped wouldn't stick. "Time to get this day started." Leola chuckled. It was something Ma always said on special days. A wave of homesickness washed over her. "No time for homesickness now. I've a job to do."

Leola and Wilma hurried the short distance to the school after a quick breakfast. "Remember to get the upper hand with your students today, Leola. Don't let them think you're nice. If you do, they'll run all over you."

Leola mumbled a quiet thank you, knowing she wouldn't follow Wilma's advice. *Why wouldn't students want to know they have a nice teacher?*

Standing at her classroom, she eagerly waited for the arrival of her students. Nervous twitters moved in her stomach like flitting sparrows searching for seeds. *My goodness, Leola. Why are you so nervous? It's not like this is the first time you've taught children.* She took a deep breath and whispered a quick prayer just as she saw a trio walking up the path to her classroom.

"I'm Lucinda Willett. This here's Mary Alice and Adam. Mary Alice's in fifth and she won't be givin' you any trouble. Adam's in seventh. He can git rambunctious at times. If you have any trouble with him, jist let me know and I'll make sure 'hit stops." With that, she turned abruptly and head back down the path.

Leola directed the two children to their seats, then turned back to see a mother bustling up the sidewalk with what seemed to be one of her older students. Leola hid a smile at the obvious embarrassment of the older student whose mom escorted him to school. Before she could offer a greeting, the mom began to talk.

"I'm Marion Graves. You've met my husband, Joseph Graves, the school board treasurer. This is our son, William. William's an eighth grader and we expect him to be ready for high school next year. We'll be taking him to Jasper to live with my parents so he can attend a high school. Your job's to make sure he's prepared. My Joseph will be stopping by from time to time to see how he is doing in class." She turned to leave, then paused and faced Leola again. "We expect him to be top of his class at graduation time."

Leola and William watched as the mother hurried down the path. The hem of her satin skirt switched back and forth, causing little puffs of dirt to dance around her walk. With a sinking heart, Leola quietly sent William to his desk in the back of the room as another parent approached with a young girl and an older boy.

"Don't let Marion bother you none. She mostly bark and no bite. I reckon the lady's forgotten to be thankful for all she has. My name's Racheal Carter. This here's Hal, he's a fifth grader. This is Civil Mae, my first grader. I'll be takin' her to the other classroom."

Racheal gave Leola a warm smile and continued, "I'm wantin' you to know I'll be praying for both my kid's teachers this year. If there's anything you're needin', jist let me know. Well, I'd best git Civil Mae to her class. She plenty nervous 'bout her first day of school."

Leola watched the mother head toward the other classroom. Big crocodile tears threatened to spill down Civil Mae's cheeks. *Lord, please let Wilma be kind to this little girl.*

Soon, kids piled in at such a fast rate, Leola had no time to think about Mrs. Graves or Civil Mae. Glancing around the room between arrivals, she was pleased to note how quiet the students were, although they had plenty of quick glances at their new teacher.

The morning flew by as Leola passed out books and explained daily routines. After lunch, she gave each of her students paper and pencil. "Please write an essay about your favorite day of the summer." A few low grumbles followed but soon enough the class settled into the project. All Leola heard was the scratching of pencil on paper. Tonight, she would read the essays, hoping to gain insight about her students.

Her heart sank when she picked up William's paper. Clearly, he struggled to get words on paper. The childish handwriting contained several misspelled words. *Oh, dear. I may have a difficult time getting this young man ready for high school.*

By lunch, Leola had learned the names of her twelve students, and knew who were the more advanced students and those that might need extra help. She discovered the class clown when a sparrow flew through the open door and made a sweep around the classroom. A seventh-grader named Hal put his pencil box on his head, then held his arms out and bent upward, calling out in a sing-song voice, "Hey, little birdie. I'm a tree. Come nest in me."

Leola laughed with the rest of her students, then put on a serious face. "Thank you, Hal, for a fine example of poetry, though it seemed a bit short. Maybe you'd like to write three more verses as homework tonight." With that, the class went back to work, not wanting to risk the possibility that they might all be given extra writing homework.

The rest of the day passed quickly as Leola started her students on some basic math exercises. A quick glance at William's paper and she knew he struggled with math also. Could she have him ready for high school? His parents' expectations lay heavy on her mind as she closed her door at the end of the day.

By Friday, Leola's class had settled into a pleasant rhythm. Her students were respectful to her and kind to their classmates. When Leola went to bed at the end of the first week, she knelt in prayer. "Lord, I'm thanking you for such a good class. Seems like a lot to ask after you blessing me with this class, but could you help me with William? Please show me how to help him learn."

Chapter Thirteen

Otis arrived on a dreary Monday. Leola's students were reacting to the chilly, sunless day by being slow to respond. They reminded her of snails crossing a wide road.

Desperate to liven up her class, Leola announced, "I don't think we'll be able to go out for recess today, so be thinking about what you'd like to play inside the room."

"Teacher, we don't never play inside on rainy days. We just work."

Leola smiled at the boy whom she knew loved to play ball during recess. And he was good at it, better than any of the other boys. Yet, Hal patiently adapted his game to the lesser skills of his classmates.

"We don't *ever* play inside on rainy days, Hal."

"Ain't that what I said?"

Leola suppressed a smile. It would take time to help her students with grammar. Until then, she must try to not confuse them.

"Never mind, Hal. At recess time, I'm sure we can think of an inside game. Maybe Duck, Duck, Goose, Goose."

Hal smiled broadly. "Teacher, I don't see we got us any ducks or geese in this classroom, but I'd be happy to go over to the feedstore and see iff'n Mr. West would loan us a few."

The class erupted in laughter, each offering different ideas for what the game might be. Leola let them go on, happy to see them engaged for the first time this day.

Without warning, the door opened. A tall blond-headed boy with a smaller girl in bright red pigtails stood frozen near the doorway. Dressed in old clothes several sizes too big for their thin bodies, they embodied the opposite of most of Leola's students.

One by one, the students grew silent. Soon it was only those students closest to Leola who were still discussing the recess game. Aware the talking had lessened, Leola glanced around the room, her sight finally landing at the door.

She took in the children quickly: a sullen-faced boy, body tense as if ready to fight anyone who dared to approach him, and a downcast little girl who stared at her bare feet.

Leola rose from her desk. She instinctively knew her first words to these children would be important. "Hello. I'm Miss Swilley. I hope you're here to join our class." She smiled, careful not to approach too quickly.

"Name's Otis Willett. This here's Jewel. She don't

talk none. My pa told us to come to school." He flexed his fingers, drawing them into fists, his chin thrust forward.

Leola walked toward the pair. "Welcome, Otis and Jewel. Why don't you sit on the bench near the door? I'll get the class started on an assignment, then we'll talk."

Otis paused, giving a darting glance back to the door. Sighing, he took Jewel's hand and moved her to the bench. They sat stiff as boards, Jewel's eyes still on her feet. The boy continued to scan the room.

"Please take out your math books and your slates. Work on the next few pages from where you last stopped. Elizabeth and Sarah, help the younger students."

Leola returned to her desk, grabbing her roster book and a pen. She moved to the bench, taking a seat next to Jewel. "Can you tell me your age and the last grade you attended?"

Jewel glanced up then back to her feet.

"I done tol' you she cain't talk none."

Leola decided to let the matter drop for now. "Well, Otis, maybe you can tell me about your sister and yourself."

"We ain't been to school in a while now. Reckon last time we went Jewel be in third and I be in fifth. We move a lot. Only here now 'cause Ma put up such a fuss with Pa. He don't think we need no more learnin'. Reckon I'm a-thinkin' the same."

"Well, you're here now and I'm glad to have the pair of you. Why don't you try us out for a few days to see if it's a fit? You can always stop coming, although I think you might not be wanting to disappoint your Ma." Leola watched Otis, eager to see the young boy's reaction.

He looked down at the floor, then scanned the room once again. "Reckon I could give it a try. Jist don't care much for learnin' or snotty-nosed kids who're thinkin' their better 'n us."

"Good, let's give it a few weeks. See if we can find some learning you might like."

Otis's shoulders relaxed slightly as he gave Leola a quick nod.

Leola took Jewel's hand. "Otis, you take the seat there next to Delbert. He's in sixth grade. I'll place you for now. Jewel, come with me and I'll introduce you to Christine and Sarah. They help me with the fourth graders. They'll show you where to start with your math."

Leola turned to the rest of the class. "I'd like the seventh graders to bring their readers to the long table. The rest of you continue with your math assignments."

Her hands trembled as she directed Jewel over to her two helpers. Something about Otis made the hairs at the nape of her neck lift. *Goodness, why am I so nervous? Nothing unusual about getting a couple of new students.*

Leola struggled the rest of the day. The dreary day added a slow drizzle to its mix around midmorning. The kids went from despondent to irritable. Leola's attempt at a game of Duck, Duck, Goose, Goose only increased the poor attitudes. Mary tripped and hurt her knee when she called "Duck, Duck, Goose, Goose" on Asberry. He caught up with her so quickly, she tripped headfirst into three other students causing loud squabbles to erupt. Otis refused to play, choosing to stand over the game with his fists curled in a clear message for no one to harm Jewel.

Leola made every effort to help Otis feel a part of the class, only to watch him resist. The tension in his body grew as the day drug on. Hours later Jewel still hadn't spoken a word, although she sat doing her work at what appeared to be a solid fourth grade level. Leola breathed a sigh. *I'm glad I didn't have to send her to Wilma as a third grader.*

By the end of the day, Leola's nerves were frazzled. She walked slowly home in the drizzling rain, replaying the day. The combination of bad weather and new students put the class into freefall of poor behavior. By the time she reached the boarding house, she had decided this might be one of the times she'd ask Wilma for help.

"I made us chicken soup. Nothing better in this miserable kind of weather. I'm taking some over to Ellie Smith after we finish our meal. Poor soul, she and two of her littles are down with a cold." Then Mrs. Crawford quietly finished her meal.

That would be the perfect time to talk with Wilma.

"Wilma, could we have some time in the parlor right after dinner? I have a few questions." Leola kept her eyes squarely on Wilma's, willing her to react kindly.

Wilma returned the stare, pausing for a long moment. "I suppose it has something to do with your two new students. I saw them out my window when they walked up to the school. I'd say they're trouble. Best thing for you would be if they don't stay long. Most of their kind don't."

"Does this mean you'll help me or not?"

"Yes, I'll help, but I can't dawdle. I've plenty of grading to do."

Leola spent the rest of the meal silently praying her time with Wilma would be helpful and maybe break the coldness between the two.

Sitting under the glow of two electric lamps, Leola placed her eyes on Wilma, who had chosen to stand. She decided to start out humble, even though the thought of appearing weak before Wilma irked her.

"You saw the brother and sister, Wilma. They looked so lost. The boy, Otis, seems full of anger. Suddenly, my whole class changed. It's like they were scared but determined to somehow get a rise out of him. How am I going to teach with this going on? And Jewel—I don't know if she can't or just won't talk."

"I've already told you you're too soft. You need to get tough and stay tough. It's what they get at home, I'm sure. Treat them like they're used to being treated. Use a rod on the boy if he mouths you. Set the girl in the corner and don't let her up until she talks." Wilma's arms were wrapped tightly around her chest, her face red, her eyes squinted. She left the parlor without another word.

Leola's eyes followed her up the stairs. Suddenly, she knew her fellow teacher was as angry as her new student. Whatever "toughness" Otis and Jewel now faced had once happened to Wilma. Leola was sure of it.

Chapter Fourteen

School days once filled with the melodious beat between learning and laughter were now filled with irritable, bickering students. No longer did they approach their lessons as exciting learning challenges. Now they refused to attempt even the simplest task.

Leola knew her students could learn. She pondered why they were now defiant and disrespectful. In her heart, she knew. Otis spent every hour of the day with his jaws locked tight and his hands quick to curl into fists. His behavior affected all the students in the class.

Henry, a bright student and exceptional in math, tried many times to help Otis with his figures. Each time, Otis bowed up with a vengeance. Henry eventually gave up and ignored him, even though they shared the same desk.

Leola didn't blame him or any of the other students who were giving Otis a wide berth. She wanted to do the same. The undercurrent of hatred residing beneath the boy's hard eyes threatened to boil up at any moment. He reminded her of a rattlesnake, coiled and ready to strike.

Letters from home became the only brightness in Leola's long days. She rushed to the mercantile which held the local post office as soon as the school day ended. If she had a letter, she'd return to her boarding house and devour it in the confines of her room.

Ma wrote once a week, letting the older kids add a few lines, and she always included a hello from Pa. The crippling homesickness from back in September lessened when Leola's teaching days were flowing well. Now, with her class in a mess, the longing for home returned, robbing her sleep and leaving her exhausted each day.

Leola tacked a John Deere calendar Mr. West had given her on the wall beside her bed. Each night before turning off her lamp, she marked off the day, counting the remaining days until Christmas when she could travel back home. She struggled to write letters to the family. What could she say? Certainly nothing positive about her students, and she couldn't share about her poor relationship with Wilma. *Seems like all I can talk about is the weather and good things from church.*

Sundays became Leola's favorite day. Today she sat in the pew alongside Mrs. Crawford singing gospels and anticipating hearing the sermon. She stopped singing and began reflecting on her life. Leola whispered softly, "Where has my joy gone, Father? Seems every day but Sunday is a struggle."

The song leader called for page 231, *His Eye is on the Sparrow*. Instead of singing the familiar words, Leola listened to the words. Bits and pieces of the song flowed into her bruised heart like a healing balm.

Why should I feel discouraged,
why should the shadows come,
Why should my heart be lonely,
and long for heaven and home,
When Jesus is my portion?
My constant friend is He:
His eye is on the sparrow,
and I know He watches me;
His eye is on the sparrow,
and I know He watches me.

"Let not your heart be troubled,"
His tender word I hear,
And resting on His goodness,
I lose my doubts and fears;
Though by the path He leadeth,
but one step I may see;
His eye is on the sparrow,
and I know He watches me;
His eye is on the sparrow,
and I know He watches me.

Her eyes filled with tears as she prayed. "Lord, I've been selfish, wanting my class to be my way. Help me see You as my portion and know You're watching over me. Heal my broken spirit and return my joy."

She looked around, wondering if others heard her prayer. But it didn't matter. Her heart was lighter than it had been in weeks. She continued her whispered prayer. "Thank You for being my friend. Help me seek Your purpose for me and for those around me."

Leola could hardly wait for the preaching to be over and the end of the service. Joy filled her soul, along with a desire to soak up the beauty of the day. As soon as the service was over, she turned to Mrs. Crawford. "Please excuse me from lunch. I'd like to take a walk along the creek and see the red and gold fall colors."

She turned to see Wilma, head down, hurrying out the of the church. "I'll ask Wilma to go with me. Would you excuse both of us?"

"Of course. I'll put you each a plate in the pie safe. You girls go and enjoy your afternoon."

Leola hurried to catch up with Wilma. "Wilma, would you like to take a walk with me? It's a beautiful day. Let's go down by the creek. I really want to be outside, but I probably shouldn't wander so far alone. The school board may not like it."

It seemed Wilma might say no. Then, Leola watched as Wilma's eyes drifted toward the woods.

"I'll go with you if you're sure you want me." Wilma's eyes were apprehensive.

"I'm sure." Leola flashed a big smile. "It would be a shame to waste a beautiful day like this sitting in the house."

Soon, they were out of the town and making their way toward the creek. The deep golds and reds of the oaks painted a watercolor against the blue skies.

Scents of pine needles and pine tar enveloped the air. Leola watched Wilma's tension melt away like an icicle melts in the sunshine.

"Used to spend as much time outside as I could. Seemed to soothe me. I always thought it might be the best place to find God," Wilma shared as she spanned the area near the creek, spotting a man and a dog skirting the other side of the creek bed, just beyond yelling distance. She nodded her head in his direction. "I don't recall seeing him in church this morning. I reckon he likes to find God outside too."

Leola glanced across the creek, surprised to see the man from the woods. *Why wasn't he in church this morning?* Leola turned her gaze back to the ground. *Why does it seem to matter to me?*

Hoping to take advantage of the relaxed moment between them, Leola decided to take a chance. "Wilma, will you help me this afternoon? I need to order a new winter coat. Mine is back home and I already told Ma to cut it down to fit my next youngest sister. I know Mrs. Crawford will loan us her Sears Roebuck catalog. I'd like help picking out the right coat. It's hard to tell from a picture."

"I'm not much good at picking out clothes. But I can help you with the cost. I know how to economize."

Leola and Wilma spent a full hour perusing through the catalog, comparing the looks and prices of every coat. With the decision made, Leola turned to the dresses. She pointed to a dark rust-colored dress with ruffles around the neck and a deep ruffle at the hem.

"This would look wonderful on you, Wilma. The

color would go well with your hair color."

The change in Wilma was immediate and chilling. The relaxed lines around her eyes and mouth returned to the hardness Leola knew from their first meeting.

"My pa would never let me have something so frilly. He'd take a cane to me if he saw me in it." She rose quickly and headed to her room without another word.

Chapter Fifteen

Leola set out for school the next morning with a with a lighter step. The day brightened even more when Hal handed her a note from his mother.

Miss Swilley, we'd be pleasured to have you take supper with us tonight. Walk home with Hal and Civil Mae. Rachel Carter

Excitement coursed through Leola, welcoming the idea of getting to know her students and their parents better. At morning recess, she told Wilma about the invitation.

Wilma frowned. "I think it's a mistake to accept the invitation. It's not good to get close to any of the students' families."

Leola paused. How could she make Wilma understand what her heart was telling her? She knew God's hand was in this visit. She would follow His lead and let Him do whatever work He was starting.

"Please tell Mrs. Crawford it won't be a habit. I

know she prepares enough food for the three of us. I don't take her efforts lightly." She took Civil Mae's hand. "Come, dear. I'm going to walk home with you today."

Hal led the way out of town until it opened into a clearing, just a half mile from the school. There stood an unpainted house with a wide porch, filled with rockers. The yard, surrounded by a wooden fence, showed signs of care. Inside the fence, four big pecan trees were shedding their fall leaves, proof of winter's approach.

Leola stopped and for a moment she was back home. She blinked rapidly when tears gathered behind her eyes, not wanting to confuse Civil Mae with her emotions.

"Let's go, Civil Mae. I'll bet your mama could use some help with supper."

Rachel met them on the porch, wiping her hands on a red and white striped dishtowel. "Come on in, Miss Swilley. I'm just getting the biscuits rolled out. You can help with the cutting. Shore glad you came. Been wantin' to have you, just seems like time gets away with me."

Rachel glanced down at her daughter. "Civil Mae, you go change out of your school dress, then you can help set the table."

Lightheaded at the thought of working in the kitchen alongside Rachel, gratitude filled Leola's heart like well water fills a bucket—to the brim. *Thank You, Lord, for knowing what I sorely missed. Thank You for using this kind lady to give it to me.*

"I'd be happy to help with those biscuits. I always cut Ma's for her. And please call me Leola."

"Call me Rachel. I'm not sure my biscuits will

stand up to your Ma's, but my man, Silas, has been eatin' them for the last ten years so they must have some good in 'em."

Silas stepped onto the porch from the steps. "I'd say they've more than good in 'em. 'Bout the best I've ever ate. Especially when you put some of your famous dewberry jelly on 'em."

Rachel swiped at her husband with her dishtowel. "Ah, go on with you. I reckon after a day workin' at the sawmill, dirt would taste good to you."

Silas turned to Leola. "Mighty nice to meet you, Miss Swilley. My kids been talkin' plenty about you. This here's my cousin, John Thomas. He's livin' with us while he works with me at the mill."

Behind him stood the man from the woods. Leola's muscles went stiff and her mouth suddenly went dry, preventing her from saying a word.

Thank goodness Hal and Civil Mae appeared on the porch, determined to play with the man's ever-present hound dog. No one noticed the awkward moment.

John Thomas spoke first. "'Hit's nice to meet you, Miss Swilley. Been meaning to come by and check the water buckets at the school. I'm thinkin' one of them might need replacing." Leola saw him working his face muscles to keep from smiling.

She swallowed a gasp. *How dare he talk about the water bucket!* She tipped her head at the man, then spun around. "I think Rachel needs help with her biscuits."

The meal of venison stew in a rich deep brown gravy, collard greens, roasted sweet potatoes and fluffy, steaming biscuits looked delicious but held no taste for Leola. She was acutely aware of the man sitting across the table next to Hal. Civil Mae sat beside her with Silas and Rachel at each end. Ten-month-old Polly sat in her mama's lap. Rachel kept the conversation going, talking about her day and asking their kids about their school day.

Civil Mae began squirming when Rachel brought a freshly baked dewberry cobbler to the table. "Is it time, Cousin John Thomas?"

"Not yet, Half-Pint. Reckon the cobbler needs a little attention right now." These were the first words he'd spoken since he sat down for the meal.

Frowning, Civil Mae began eating the cobbler at lightning speed, getting deep purple berry juice all over her mouth.

John Thomas laughed. "You look like you been caught in the berry patch, Half-Pint."

Leola glanced at the man who'd just spoken. *It's a nice laugh.* The water bucket suddenly came to mind and she cast her eyes back to her plate. *I won't let myself get fooled over a nice laugh!*

Soon, the cobbler was a mere memory, and everyone pushed back from the table.

John Thomas grabbed for his hat. "Reckon I'd better take this young'un out to see the new litter of pups. She's not gonna let up till I do."

"Yea!" Civil Mae exclaimed. "You come too, Teacher. They's jist born last week and they's sooo cute."

Leola froze. She'd loved nothing more than when a new litter was born at the farm back home. She found many excuses to go to the barn for an opportunity to cuddle soft coats and stare into bright eyes. But there was no way she was going anywhere with John Thomas. She grabbed two plates and headed for the sink. "Thanks, but I need to stay here and help your mama with the dishes."

"No, you don't. You're a guest." Rachel took the plates from her hands. "Reckon I can handle these dishes on my own. I do most every night. You go see those pups. Civil Mae ain't gonna be happy till you do. Best to hurry. It'll be gettin' dark soon."

Trapped, Leola turned and followed Civil Mae out the door. *I'll just ignore him, that's what I'll do. I won't let him keep teasing me!*

The trio walked silently down a small hill behind the house. At the bottom were many sets of pens, some holding single male dogs, others holding mama dogs with pups of varying ages.

"Goodness. I've never seen so many dogs in one place."

"Silas sells them as trained hunting dogs to men all over this county and several other counties. He's known to be one of the best breeders in the area. Been helpin' him do some trainin' when I have time. Learned a lot about the business already. Reckon I might try my hand at it one day soon. That pen with the newest litter is mine." John Thomas breathed a deep breath.

Leola suspected it was a longer speech than he generally made. She focused on the penned dogs, saying nothing.

"Reckon I got me another reason to apologize.

I'm right sorry I brought up the water bucket."

Leola looked up at his face, and once again his eyes caught and held her attention. Those soft hazel eyes spoke volumes of kindness.

Suddenly, a bubbly laugh escaped her lips. "Well, I guess I did look a might awkward standing on a water bucket, then tumbling to the ground."

"Reckon you did, but it don't excuse rudeness none. Must be a flaw in my character. I seem to git along better with hound dogs than humans."

Their words suddenly dried up like a shallow pond in the summer heat. Thank goodness Civil Mae had enough words for everyone. "Look-it, Teacher. Cousin John Thomas says this is the best one." She held the pup out to Leola. "His name is Pick cause he's the pick of the litter."

Grabbing the squiggly pup before he hurled to the ground, Leola held him close to her neck. Compared to the others, she could see why this pup was the pick. With a long body, well-shaped head, and defined muscles, Leola knew instinctively he would be a good stud when he was grown.

Curious, she forgot her resolve to ignore. "Where'd you get their mama? Is she from one of Silas's litters?"

"Oh, no. She's a German shorthaired pointer. I ordered her from the Sears Roebuck catalog. Picked her up at the train in Newton 'bout ten months ago. One of Silas's bluetick coonhounds bred her. This here's her first litter. So far, she ain't disappointin' me none."

"You ordered her from Sears Roebuck catalog?"

"Yep. You gotta get past ladies wear to find the dogs," a grin played at John Thomas's lips.

"Yer welcome to come anytime to visit the pups. The more they're handled, the better they git at acceptin' human commands. Reckon you'd be doing me a favor. We'd best be gettin' back to the house. Sun'll drop soon."

Leola ducked her head, surprised to be invited to come back to see his dogs. *Why does he always make my head spin?*

At the house, Leola grabbed her teaching bag. Rachel instructed Hal to walk his teacher home, which he did willingly, knowing he could take one of his dad's hounds and do some tracking on the way back.

Darkness set in just as Leola entered the boarding house. Wilma met her in the hallway on her way upstairs.

"You're back. I'm guessing it was a tedious meal, what with having the parents grilling you about their kids' performance at school." Wilma's face puckered. "I'm thinking you understand now why I thought it a bad idea to go."

Leola smiled as she followed Wilma up the stairs. "Actually, it was a wonderful evening. I played with puppies." *And I talked with the man from the woods.*

Chapter Sixteen

Soon the vibrant red and gold colors of autumn gave way to the bleakness of late fall. Leola was sad to miss Thanksgiving with her family, but two days off school didn't allow time for the long trip home.

Mrs. Crawford served a wonderful meal and Leola passed the long afternoon by the fire shelling pecans for the Christmas holiday baking. She even managed to get Wilma to join her at the task.

After a light supper of leftovers, Mrs. Crawford suggested a game of Hearts.

"I'd love to. I play with my older siblings back home. But I warn you, I play to win!" Leola grinned and turned to Wilma. "How about you? Would you like to make it a threesome?"

Wilma rose with force, almost tumbling her chair to the floor. "I'll never have idle hands playing a game of cards." Leola and Mrs. Crawford watched her stiff back as she hurriedly exited the parlor.

"Poor soul," Mrs. Crawford sighed. "It's almost like she's afraid to have fun."

Freezing rain arrived the Monday after Thanksgiving. Leola shivered when her bare feet hit the floor in the early morning hours. She groaned, dreading the cold walk to school to start the fires in her room and in Wilma's. Every time she thought of telling Wilma it should be a shared job, God gently stopped her. *Be a servant.*

She tiptoed over to her dresser and read the handwritten scripture taped to her mirror.

You will go out with joy and be led forth in peace. Isaiah 55:12

She stared at the scripture once more. *It's hard to be joyful about tending to the fires on this cold day.* Her thoughts turned to Otis. She still struggled with his behavior. Yet, she knew God was doing a work in Otis and she was willing to wait until He brought about His plan.

Since the day at church when God talked to her heart, peace had been her companion. Stopping to say a quick prayer before heading down the stairs, Leola whispered words bringing certainty and comfort. *Thank you, Father, that my peace is from You, not my circumstances. Thank You for the sweet joy in my life.*

Chilly wind and freezing rain made her hurry along the path to the school, keeping her head down to avoid the hard, frozen pellets from hitting her face. Trying to think of something other than her cold feet, she imagined her upcoming trip home. More content now, she no longer marked off the days on her calendar. But as Christmas approached her excitement grew as she pictured the decorations, the food, and her siblings' giddiness, things which marked every Christmas holiday in her memory.

As soon as she felt the pebble path leading to the school, she lifted her head and hurried to her door, thankful she had replenished the wood stacked in the corner of the room before the Thanksgiving break.

Opening the door, warm air hit first her face, then slowly warmed the rest of her chilly body. Surprised, she turned to see a roaring fire in the woodstove. The room was toasty and ready for her students.

Quickly, she rushed outside, careful not to slip on the frozen steps, and opened the door to Wilma's room. The same warm flush of air told Leola that Wilma's stove was also lit. Amazement and gratitude filled her soul. "Lord, I don't know who did this, but please bless their day because they've surely blessed mine."

By mid-week the freezing snow turned to heavy snow. All week Leola rose early enough to be at school in time to start the fires, only to find the rooms already warm. She didn't tell anyone what was happening. Her imagination went into action, conjuring up everything from elves to fairies to a Good Samaritan.

On Friday, she was surprised to see Wilma already at the table when she arrived for her early breakfast. She paused, not sure what to say.

Wilma kept her eyes on a bowl of oatmeal. "Reckon our rooms will have more time to warm up if we start the fires at the same time. I'll walk over with you." She resumed eating, not giving Leola a chance to answer.

Leola's emotions were mixed. Elated Wilma wanted to extend this act of friendship, she didn't know what she'd say if the fires were already lit. She mumbled a quick thank you and quietly ate her breakfast.

Explanations for why the fires may be lit swarmed in Leola's head like locust in a wheat field. *If they're lit, how am I going to explain it? I doubt Wilma will accept a miracle.* Before they reached the classroom doors, Leola turned to Wilma. "Wilma, I need to tell you something about..."

"We can talk after the fires are going. It's silly to talk in this cold," Wilma headed into her classroom, with Leola right behind her. Once inside, Wilma stopped and stared.

"This is what I wanted to tell you. Something—I mean someone—has been starting the fires all week. I didn't know how to tell anyone."

Wilma walked over to the front window, staring down at the snow leading to the woods. When she turned around, a small smile played on her lips. "Well, it sure isn't an angel, unless they come with boots and paws."

Leola made her way to the window. The start of a new day cast just enough light to make out prints headed away from the schoolhouse. She knew of only one person who always had a dog at his heels. She dipped her face downward until she was sure Wilma wouldn't see the pink flush spreading across her cheeks.

Chapter Seventeen

Leola sat by the fire on Christmas Eve, warmed more by being with her family than by the flames. The day had been perfect with clear blue skies and an unusually warm temperature for December. After helping Ma cook all morning, Leola escaped the kitchen long enough to play with her sibling in the yard. Now, with supper over, she and the rest of the family sat stringing popcorn for the Christmas tree. A pine tree sat in the corner of the front room, waiting to be decorated.

"Leola, seems to me you're extry quiet t'night. Somethin' on your mind?" Ma set down her coffee cup and looked at her daughter.

Leola ducked her head. She'd been thinking about the Carters and wondering if John Thomas might be stringing popcorn with Hal and Civil Mae. Guilt lay heavily on her stomach, making her wish she hadn't eaten so much of the popcorn in her bowl. *What's the matter with me? I couldn't wait to get home and now all*

I can do it think of everyone back in Springtown—and, truth be known, of the man from the woods. I'm not ready to share about John Thomas yet.

"Nothing on my mind, Ma. I'm just thinking about how nice it is to be back home."

"Daughter, I never left my home except when I got married and then it be only from one farm to another not ten miles away. I'm figurin' 'hits okay to be wantin' to be in two places at once."

Not trusting her voice, she smiled weakly and nodded. Desperate to change the subject, she called out to her youngest brother. "Young man, our Christmas tree is going to be almost bare if you don't stop eating all the popcorn!"

With no garden to tend, the week after Christmas offered Leola time to work on her lessons. Each morning, she helped Ma with the breakfast dishes and straightened the bedrooms and front room. Then she spread out her poetry books, intent on preparing a poetry unit for her students. She decided to use the poems of Henry Wadsworth Longfellow and searched out the poems filled with nature. Her students would identify with the poet's descriptions of forests, creeks, and wildlife.

"Leola, I'm thinkin your hands are goin' to wrinkle like a prune iff'n you don't get done with those dishes." Ma stood with her hands on her hips.

Leola jerked back to the present, realizing she'd been standing thinking with her hands emerged in the dishwater, the lukewarm water a tell-tale sign she'd been this way for quite a while.

"I'm sorry, Ma. I don't mean to be distant. I feel like I have two lives now. Just don't know which one I'm in sometimes."

Ma squeezed her arm. "That's all right, Daughter. I reckon you're jist feelin' some growin' pains. God will show you the path He has for you."

January passed slowly, bringing bleak days filled with a mix of snow and freezing rain. Leola could sleep later now, knowing the fires in both classroom rooms would be lit and she would arrive to a warm, cozy room.

On a rainy cold day in late January, Leola pulled out a 1925 almanac she'd gotten at the mercantile store. Mr. West had also given her several pamphlets on farming and animal husbandry. She hoped William might read better if it was something he was interested in. While the other students were reading to each other in pairs, she put William to the task of reading the almanac and pamphlets. To her surprise, William focused on the information with a determination she'd not seen before. He still struggled with some words, but she could hear his reading improving rapidly.

"I like this kind of readin', Teacher. Hit's more fun than reading those stories in the reader." William's smile spread from ear to ear. "I'm thinkin' I almost sound like the other eighth graders."

Encouraged, she offered to let him take a few of the pamphlets home to read each night, knowing the more he read, the better he'd become. She planned to spend several evenings writing math problems about farming and farm animals, hoping this might improve his math.

Another surprise came when she introduced the poetry unit. While reading *Paul Revere's Ride*, Otis listened with intensity, his eyes less hard and his body not resonating with anger. She kept reading, not willing to see the old Otis return. She moved on to *The Song of Hiawatha*, pleased to see Otis even more engrossed by the Indian legends.

For the rest of the day Otis seemed less angry and more ready to attempt his lessons. At the end of the day, Leola held out the book holding the poem about Hiawatha. "Would you like to take this home to read the rest of the poem? You can bring it back when you're finished. Maybe we can talk about it and you can share what you read with the class."

Otis looked at the book like it might bite him. "You meanin' it, Teacher?"

"Yes, Otis. We have other poems to study. We've finished with what I wanted to share from this poem."

Otis grabbed the book, hugging it to his chest. "I'll be takin' good care of it."

John Thomas stopped, careful not to crunch the brush under him when his dog took a stance. Something had his dog on point, but he didn't think it was a deer or hog. He listened for a moment, then heard an angry voice. Giving the order for his dog to stay, he quietly walked closer until he could see.

"I'm tellin' you, boy. You take that sissy poem

book back to that teacher and tell 'er I don't hold with no teachin' about Injuns. You tell 'er she better watch out for herself. I might want to find 'er alone somewhere. Man's gotta stand up when sumpin' is wrong—and teaching the stuff she's teachin's wrong." The words spewed from Mr. Willett's mouth.

Through the trees, John Thomas could see Otis's father squeezing his son's arm with one hand while his other hand pulled on a mass of his hair. Otis moaned in pain but managed to say "Y'sir, Pa."

John Thomas planted his feet wide, ready to step in to help Otis, but his father let go of him and stomped off spouting a string of curse words. Leaning down to the pup, John Thomas stroked the dog's fur and whispered, "I reckon we better keep an eye on Miss Leola."

The Willett kids had not been to school since Leola gave Otis the poem book. She waited several days, then decided to visit Rachel. Since both Hal and Civil Mae had been sick with the flu, she wanted to see if Rachel knew if there had been flu at the Willett's also.

She walked across the field, approaching the woods when John Tomas suddenly joined her, matching his stride to hers.

"I'm sorry, but you can't walk with me. It's against the school board rules. But I'd like to thank you for starting our fires each morning." She smiled into John Thomas's face, once again absorbed by his eyes.

"Don't know nothin' about those fires. I reckon the school board will understand just this once iff'n I walk you to wherever you're goin'." John Thomas looked over his shoulder toward the woods.

Leola followed his gaze in time to see Otis melting into some thicket under the pines. A tingling started at her feet, zinging its way to the hairs on her head. Had Otis intended to harm her?

Early the next morning, she was surprised to see Otis walk into the classroom. He was once again the child who had entered her classroom back in the fall. Hardness filled his eyes and his body. He handed her the book and blurted out, "Pa's agin' me readin' this. Wants us home. Says what you're teachin's wrong." He turned and strode from the room. Just outside the door, he turned back to Leola.

"Weren't follerin' you the other day to hurt you none, Teacher." Then he turned and ran off into the woods.

Leola's heart fell into a deep hole. "How could this poem offend Mr. Willett, and why was Otis holding his right arm?" She had no answers, but she was determined to find out. She wasn't going to let Otis and Jewel stay home. "It's time for a home visit!"

She needed to talk with Mr. Willett but the thought of being face to face with him made her stomach turn into a hard rock. *Maybe Rachel will go with me since she's the closest neighbor to the Willett's.* She sent a note home with Hal asking if she could visit the next afternoon.

Hall approached her desk the next morning. "Ma says she'd be pleased to have you and that you gotta stay to supper."

Leola smiled, wondering when she'd ever get her students to use correct grammar. She notified Wilma that she'd be at the Carter's home for supper. This time Wilma nodded her head with no comments. Gratitude swelled up in Leola, seeing the more likable Wilma.

As she set out on the walk to the Carter's, she fell behind Hal and Civil Mae. Both confusion and anticipation filled her thoughts. *Did I do this just to see John Thomas? I wish I had fixed my hair better this morning.*

Leola helped make the biscuits and soon she was sitting at the table, very aware of the man sitting across from her. Again, Rachel led most of the conversation.

When there was a break in the talking, Leola turned to Civil Mae. "Would you like to go see the pups when we finish our meal?"

"Can't, they're gone. Cousin John Thomas gave..."

"More eaten', less talkin', Half-Pint." They were the first words John Thomas had uttered since the meal began.

"But..."

"You heard your cousin, Civil Mae." Silas gave his daughter a long, hard look.

Civil Mae closed her mouth, her eyes wet with sudden tears. Confused, Leola decided it best to change the subject. She turned to Rachel. "I'm wondering if you might go with me to the Willetts' tomorrow. I need to talk to Mr. Willett. He's not letting Otis and Anna come to school. I want to see if I can change his mind."

Rachel started to respond, but John Thomas cut her off. "Miss Leola, he ain't there. He's hightailed it out of the county. His wife'll be doin' laundry for the Graves and some other families. I reckon they'll be better off with him gone."

Before Leola could question more, Rachel spoke up. "I 'spect you jist might be seein' more of the Willett kids at school now. Their ma wants 'em to git educated."

Leola wanted to ask more questions, but the dismissive tone of Rachel and John Thomas assured there would be no more discussion tonight.

She arrived back at the boarding house with more confusion than ever. Why did Mr. Willett leave, and what happened to John Thomas's dogs?

Lord, I'm not sure what's going on, but I'm trusting You have a hand in all of this.

Chapter Eighteen

By March, winter fought for control over the appearance of spring. Daffodils and crocuses forced their heads through frozen, sometimes icy, ground. Leola pulled her coat tighter as she opened her classroom door, eager to feel the warmth from the already lit fire. A noise at the door made her turn quickly to find Otis holding the hand of his younger sister. Leola tried not to react to their sudden appearance. She motioned them into the warm classroom without saying a word.

Otis spoke first. "Pa ain't here no more." He offered Leola the first ever smile. "I mean 'anymore.' You thinkin' I could have that book back for a spell?"

Holding back the desire to grab each of them in a bear hug, Leola quietly responded, "Yes, you can have the book—and welcome back."

"Can I have a book, Teacher?" Anna said softly, looking straight at Leola.

Speechless, Leola's face beamed as she nodded.

Thank you, Lord, for this child's speech, and for their return to school.

Spring finally won its battle, bringing a warmth which filled both human and plant with happiness. Leola's teaching days were no longer filled with strife. Once again, the melodious beat of learning returned, and Leola found joy in her teaching and deep affection for every student.

May brought longer days and the much-anticipated end of school picnic. Held on a Saturday, the whole town had been invited to celebrate the ending of another school year and graduation of three eighth graders.

The county superintendent of schools planned to attend to present the certificates, and the school board would be present to shake the hands of the graduates. Leola and Wilma had prepared their students to do recitations and songs before the ceremony. Wilma surprised Leola by taking the lead and helping the students learn their parts.

The day arrived with the scent-filled warm air of spring. Dogwoods and redbuds put splashes of red and white in the nearby woods. Fluffy white clouds danced across the sky and the sweet-smelling spring grass between the school and the woods provided the perfect place to spread the picnic cloths.

Leola arrived early to make sure everything was in order. She checked the certificates again and then wrote a special note inside three new copies of *The*

Adventures of Huckleberry Finn. She planned to give them to the graduates as a special gift from her.

By mid-morning, families were settled on quilts and old tablecloths spread on the grass and the superintendent took his place at a homemade podium. Wilma led the students through their rehearsed parts. Then it was time for the graduation ceremony.

Leola's heart swelled as she watched her three eighth grader students receive their certificates. She was proud of all three but more so of William. He'd worked hard and improved his reading and math skills. Leola still doubted he would make it in high school, but she knew she had done her best for him. She prayed his parents would understand his love of farming and allow him to work the family farm instead.

When the ceremony ended, families and friends spread out fried chicken, ham sandwiches, potato salad, pickled okra and beets, fried apple pies, and a variety of cakes. The sights and the smells made Leola's stomach grumble. Rachel asked Leola to join them at their picnic. Mrs. Crawford and Wilma invited John West and his three children to join them for food they had fretted over for days. Wilma especially had seemed to want it to be just right.

The day seemed perfect to Leola. Her only sadness was not seeing her friends over the summer. But she needed to be at her parents' home place for the summer to help Ma with the garden. And the school board didn't provide summer lodging for their teachers.

"Would you like to walk by the creek, Miss Leola?"

Leola looked up to see John Thomas standing over her, his hand stretched out. She glanced around to see if any school board members were close by.

"I'd like a walk. I've been sitting on the ground for quite a spell." She put her hand in his, allowing him to gently pull her to her feet.

They strolled toward the creek without speaking until Leola suddenly turned to John Thomas. "I'd like to ask you a question and I'd like an honest answer."

"Reckon I'm an honest man, Miss Leola."

Leola's stomach tightened, not sure if she should ask such a personal question. "Why aren't you a church-going man? Do you believe?"

"Reckon I been a believer for a long spell now. Jist never had no need to go to church—till now, anyways. Reckon I got me a right good reason for attending now."

"Now?"

"Yes'm. Be that pretty young woman on the third row back."

"You've been at church? But I've never..."

A grin made its way to John Thomas's face. "I reckon hits hard to see who all's there iff'n most of the people's behind you. I clear out fast enough. Never been much for socializing."

He is a believer! Why is this so important to me?

"Can I ask you another question?" A quick nod from John Thomas told her to proceed. "I'd like to know what happened to your litter of dogs."

When John Thomas hesitated, Leola thought he might not answer, but soon enough he responded.

"I'm thinkin' you oughta know. I give 'em to Otis's father on the condition he leave this county and stay gone."

Leola gasped. "But why? You were so proud of the mama and those pups."

"Bill Willett is an evil man, Leola. A danger to you and to his family. I know, I seen it first-hand."

Leola caught her breath, remembering the day Otis returned the poetry book and the arm he held close against his side. She tried to put it all together but still couldn't understand how she could be in danger.

John Thomas spoke again. "Reckon you need to hear all of it. Willett threatened to hurt you. I heard it in the woods when he was being rough with Otis. The day you saw Otis following us—he was trying to protect you, not harm you. He knew his father would be waiting to get you alone."

Leola tried to absorb the reality of the situation, unable to understand how someone could be so cruel. And how a man could give up his prized possessions just for her.

"But you gave up your hound and all of her litter, even Pick."

John Thomas took a step closer to Leola. "I'm thinkin' I can always order another dog from Sear & Roebuck. Truth be, Miss Leola, I've come to see you as the pick of the litter." He swallowed and removed his battered hat from his head. "I ain't got much to offer and I sorely ain't as educated as you, but I can promise you my love and my carin' for. I'd be honored if you'd be my wife."

Leola grabbed her torso to stop the sudden flutter in her stomach. She touched her neck as a flush of red rushed to her face. For a moment, she could only stare at John Thomas's face. Then, her eyes focused on his eyes—eyes she thought of so often. She'd fallen in love with those eyes and all that went with them.

A peace flooded her heart, sure this was God's plan for her. "I'd be honored to call you my husband, John Thomas."

Then she could no longer see the beautiful eyes as John Thomas pulled her into an embrace, giving her a gentle, lingering kiss.

Chapter Nineteen

Leola was getting married to the man from the woods. Her heart swelled with excitement, then burst like a like a dropped watermelon. *I can't teach if I'm married.* For a split-second Leola considered finding John Thomas to tell him she couldn't give up her teaching. Then words from her ma skittered across her brain. "Don't let your desires get in the way of God's plan for you, Leola." Leola's tense body relaxed as she whispered, "Thank you, Ma, for all your wisdom."

The sun cast long shows across the field when the picnickers, with full bellies and empty baskets, began to make their way home. Wilma's students hugged her good-bye with affection as Leola marveled at the change in her friend.

Back at Mrs. Crawford's home, the three women agreed they could eat nothing else after all the picnic food. By early evening they retired for the night, too tired for visiting in the parlor as had become their habit.

In her room, Leola couldn't settle. She went from her rocker to her desk and back again. She tried writing to Ma to tell her about her engagement, but her mind was too excited to generate the words. "I have to tell someone!" Wilma came to mind. But Leola wasn't for sure if Wilma would be happy for her. "It's worth a try. I can't stay in this room, that's for sure."

Wilma answered on the first knock. Her face held the hint of a smile.

Leola relaxed. "Can I come in and visit with you for a while?"

Opening the door wider, Wilma nodded her in.

Not sure where to start, Leola blurted out, "John Thomas asked me to marry him today."

Wilma's smile went from slight to full. "Well, I guess the important thing is to know what you said back."

Leola blushed and nodded her head. "I said yes. I love him, Wilma. I think it's God's will for my life." She held her breath, expecting a harsh reply at her reference to God.

"I'm happy for you, Leola. I hope you'll be happy for me."

Leola gave her a questioning look, waiting for more. She only had to wait a moment.

"Several weeks ago, John West came to see me one day after school. He said he needed help with his reading skills. Seems he struggled reading the newspaper and his bible. John asked me if I'd help him on Saturday evenings when the store closed. I wasn't sure if the school board would approve, but since his children would be there, I decided to do it."

Leola nodded, not wanting to interrupt Wilma's thoughts.

"The bible was the only thing he'd use for reading practice. I balked at first, but soon found he could be as stubborn as me. Thing is, Leola, as I taught him to read his bible, I began to hear God's Word in a fresh new way. Before long I wanted more, so I began to read every night before bed. In those words, I found what I've been searching for all my life. I found forgiveness and peace."

Leola pulled Wilma into a tight hug. "Oh, Wilma. I'm so happy for you. I wondered where you went on Saturday evenings. I thought you might be attending the ladies' sewing group."

With tears brimming in her eyes, Wilma began speaking again. "There's more. A few weeks ago, John asked me to marry him and I said yes. Just think of it, Leola, God's given me a wonderful man to love and a ready-made family. I've come to love his kids as well."

Leola had no words. She once again held her friend in a tight hug.

The next few weeks became a flurry of activity. Wilma and John were married the last Sunday in May.

Leola smiled at how lovely Wilma looked in her rust-colored dress, the very one she had refused to discuss back in January. How much things had changed for both of them both!

The couple moved quietly to the front of the church when the sermon was over and stood side-by-side waiting for the pastor to marry them in the sight of God and all who attended church this day. At the last moment, Wilma turned and motioned for John's children to join them. Hitty took a place beside her and the three boys joined their father.

Leola and Mrs. Crawford dug into their purses for a handkerchief as they tearfully watched Wilma marry her new family.

Leola sent a long letter to her ma and pa telling them of her engagement and up-coming marriage. She asked that they bless her plans and to forgive her for not asking their permission to marry.

A return letter arrived quickly. They were happy for their daughter and felt and confident of God's plan for this marriage. Pa suggested the couple come live with them until they could find a home. "There's plenty of work in the sawmills and I could use help clear-cuttin' a couple of acres," Pa wrote. Leola laughed with glee when she read the letter. To live near her family sounded wonderful. She just had to convince John Thomas. She'd tell him about Pa's offer that very evening when he came for their usual after supper walk.

"John Thomas, have you given any thought to where we might live?" Leola assumed he'd want to stay Stringtown. *Lord let him be accepting of Pa's plan for us.*

John Thomas stopped walking and removed his hat as he looked directly at Leola.

"I been meanin' to talk to you for the past week, Leola. Jist not sure how you'll take it. I got a letter from one of my cousins over in Bevins, Louisiana. Says the place my uncle had on the river road is available. He died a few months back. His son, Dewitt, wants to keep it in the family and says it's mine iff'n I want it. I need to tell you, Leola, 'hit ain't much to look at but I reckon we can fix it up a bit."

His face lit up as he continued. "The river road is the purtiest place I've ever know'd. The road goes right down to the river where fishin' is good. There's a beautiful marsh filled with cypress wood good for makin' furniture. The piney woods around the house has plenty of deer, hogs, squirrels, and coons. Think of it, Leola—I can hunt and fish every day. I'm tired of cuttin' trees and destroying forests. And the sawdust I'm breathing is beginnin' to hurt my lungs. I know we could be happy there." He looked at Leola with hopeful eyes.

Leola wanted to stomp her foot and say no. She had her heart set on moving home. Then she stared into the eyes she had fallen in love with. *How can I disappoint the man standing here with his hat in his hands so clearly pleading for me to see his wants?*

"John Thomas, I'll be happy to move to the river road with you." Her mouth said the words and she hoped her heart would quickly follow. For the third time in a single year she would move to a place she'd never seen.

Mrs. Crawford offered for Leola to stay at the boarding house as her guest until the wedding. She bustled around Leola helping with the plans, pleased to be involved. Leola sometimes smiled at her dear friend's constant chatter about the upcoming wedding.

She ordered her dress from the catalog. Made of blue cotton, it had appliqued flowers cut from the same fabric attached to the bodice and down the straight skirt. Leola smiled when it arrived, thinking of the two petticoats she had worn all school year. *No need for those ever again*.

Ma and Pa arrived the day before her for the wedding. Delighted to see them, she still dreaded telling them where she and John Thomas would live. After supper, Mrs. Crawford left Leola alone with her parents in the parlor, "So you three can have some time to visit."

Once again Pa sat on the sofa and Leola stifled a giggle, sure he preferred his rocking chair back home.

"Update us on your plans, Daughter. Will y'all be moving back home?" Pa looked hopeful, as did Ma.

"I'd love to, Pa. But John Thomas has other plans and I want to be a part of them." Leola waited for a response, but both parents sat quietly waiting for more.

She explained about the house on the river road and her future husband's desire to return to the place where his relatives lived. She tried to paint a picture of the place just as John Thomas had painted for her. Somehow, it sounded insincere no matter how hard she tried.

Ma spoke first. "Me and your pa have prayed you'd follow God's plan for your life. We got a peace about this marriage. Reckon we'll find peace with your move." Her eyes were shiny as she gave Leola a wobbly smile.

"I'm thinkin' the same, Daughter. Hit's a disappointment for sure, but we'll figure out the way to this river road of yours. And I reckon you know the way home."

Suddenly all three were on their feet, hugging tightly. Leola's heart filled with a gust of love for her parents stronger than any north wind could've brought.

John Thomas Cochran married Martha Leola Swilley on a sun-filled morning in June. Wilma and Racheal filled the inside of the church with bluebonnets, yellow wagon wheels, and white Queen Anne's lace.

The guests from the town filled the pews. A special row up front was reserved for Leola's students. As she came down the aisle on her father's arm, Leola saw Otis, hair slicked down, wearing what appeared to be a new shirt. He looked nothing like the boy who had appeared at her schoolroom door several months before.

With Wilma at her side and Curtis beside John Thomas, they said their vows. As the newlyweds turned to face the congregation as husband and wife, Wilma leaned into Leola's side. "Wait a moment before leaving." Then she moved to where Leola's students sat. At her signal, they rose and sang *God Be with You till We Meet Again.* On the last verse, Wilma motioned for the guests to join in and nodded for the couple to proceed down the aisle.

Leola walked toward the church's entrance holding her husband's arm, filled with overwhelming gratitude for this moment, knowing she'd remember it forever.

The guests made their way to Mrs. Crawford's home, where she bustled about adding the food brought by the community to the abundant amount she'd prepared. Soon the house filled with people eating anywhere they could find a place, some choosing to be on the porch and spilling over into the yard.

Before long, John Thomas found Leola among the crowd. "Reckon we'd best git on the road iff'n we want to be at the river road 'fore dark."

Leola suddenly turned shy. *Goodness, I'd forgotten all about the river road.* She nodded to her husband. "Let me tell Ma and Pa goodbye."

"No need, they're by the wagon. 'Hit's loaded and waitin' on us."

Guilty by the fact John Thomas had been loading the wagon while she visited, she followed him outside. The guests followed.

Ma and Pa stood near their wagon, filled with the bride and groom's things. Lucy stood hitched to the wagon.

Leola turned questioning eyes to Pa. "I been needin' a larger wagon for some time and I reckon I could use a younger mule too. Still plan on clearin' those two acres. We'll ride home with your Aunt Lucinda and Uncle Asberry."

Leola hugged them both, whispering a thank you. She turned and found her place in the familiar wagon behind Lucy. *I'm glad I have on old friend going with me.*

Part II

1924 – 1952

"For I know the plans I have for you," declares the Lord,
"plans to prosper you and not harm you, plans to give
you hope and a future."
Jeremiah 29:11

Chapter Twenty

My sisters and I were familiar with moving days. Our father's search for carpentry work kept us moving up and down the Texas coast. When getting a new job, he went first to find a rent house while we packed.

One move stands out in my mind. We made the four-hour drive from East Texas down south near the Gulf Coast. Dad had rented a house just two doors down from one of his great-aunts. The relative held strong beliefs about everything, most of which centered around "thou shalt not." Mom wasn't pleased about the location but didn't rock the marriage boat."

A few days after the move, Dad's great-aunt drove by our house and saw our mother sweeping the front porch wearing a pair of shorts and a sleeveless blouse. Not happy, she stopped and unleashed a torrent of condemnations at Mom regarding her outfit. She soon went on her way, leaving Mom gutted in her wake.

But not for long. Springing into action, our

determined mother soon found an available rent house and secured two movers to help with the move. By late afternoon we were packed, loaded, and making our move across town. The marriage boat had set sail!

Our father came home after work to find an empty house. The note left on the door simply stated, "We've moved. Here's the address. Come if you want."

The trip to the river road seemed endless. The hot afternoon sun beat down on the wagon and slowed Lucy's pace. Leola was sure a bunny could hop to their destination quicker. John Thomas tried to keep the conversation going but gave up after several tries. Leola couldn't muster responses. She had too much on her mind.

What have I done? Will I like this place where he's taking me? Already missing her family and friends, Leola's thoughts ran rampant, leaving her more despondent with each passing mile.

"Leola, honey, I aint' gonna hold you to this place. Iff'n you're really unhappy 'bout it, I'll turn us around right now. We'll figure out somethin' more to your likin'."

Her husband's voice shook her out of her reverie. *What's wrong with me? I love this man and should be happy no matter where we live.*

"I'll admit I'm more than a tad scared, John Thomas. But if you'll be patient, I'll try my best to be content."

"I can be patient and I'm thankin' you ag'in for

agreein' to come to the river road." He paused, then began again. "And I'm wantin' you to know I'll be a gentleman tonight, Leola."

Tonight? His words finally registered. *I've been so busy missing home I've not given a thought about tonight.* She tried to push the impending night out of her mind and made an effort to talk with John Thomas about the surrounding land, the wildlife, even wildflowers. Leola continued her chatter as they crossed the Sabine River, putting them in Louisiana.

The sun hovered close to the horizon when they turned onto the river road. Leola's eyes were drawn first to the tall, majestic pine trees lining the left side of the road.

When John Thomas stopped the wagon and announced, "This be it, Leola", she turned her eyes from the row of pines to a sad little house with a sagging porch. *Lord, help me find beauty somewhere. I don't want to hurt John Thomas.*

"It's set on some pretty land. Let's go inside to take a look before it gets dark." Leola hoped her smile was sincere.

John Thomas sprang into action. He hopped down and came around to help his bride down from the wagon. Walking up a dirt path, John Thomas opened the front door and stepped aside, motioning for Leola enter.

Letting her eyes adjust to the light before moving farther into the house, Leola realized she was standing in the front room. A fireplace covered a large portion of the smaller wall. Two windows let light in the front wall and the end wall. Leola surveyed the sparse furniture.

A lumpy gray couch and a few rockers filled the small room. Directly across from the entrance, a door lead into a bedroom. Leola stepped into the room long enough to take in a bed and wardrobe. Walking back to the front room, she turned to enter the kitchen. There she found a table with four chairs and the tiniest icebox she'd ever seen.

She turned questioning eyes to John Thomas.

"I'm told 'hits hard to find ice around here. Might can git some on trips to Merryville time to time."

She turned her attention to a cook stove and a small cabinet holding a cast-iron sink with a red water pump. A small pie safe sat on the wall near the table.

Moving back across the kitchen, she found a door leading to a bedroom with a larger bed and wardrobe. *This room must be meant for us.* She retreated back to the kitchen before John Thomas could see the blush on her cheeks.

John Thomas pointed to what appeared to be the back door. "That thar door leads to the well, two animal pens and the outhouse. I'll be makin' you a chicken pen soon as we can buy some chickens."

He turned to his new wife. "Will it do, Leola?"

Leola hesitated. "Does the well draw water?"

"It did when I tried 'hit a few weeks back."

"What about the cook stove? Does it work?"

"I'm told it works."

Leola kept her gaze on her husband, giving him a smile, this time a sincere one. "Then, it'll do."

Back outside, the couple worked together to unload the wagon before dark. John Thomas unhitched

Lucy and put her in the pen, giving the old mule oats supplied by his new father-in-law.

Back inside John Thomas was surprised to see the table laid with a cloth from Leola's keepsake trunk. When he stared at the flowers in a mason jar, Leola laughed. "Better get used to flowers in the house. I'm partial to them. These are honeysuckle I found climbing the side of the house by the back door. They sure do smell good."

She could see her husband relaxing as they sat down for the first meal in their new home. Leola hesitated, not sure about asking her husband to say grace.

John Thomas pleased her when he removed his hat and began to pray. "Lord, I'm thankin' You for my new wife and the place You've given us to live. And I'm thankin' You for Mrs. Crawford who packed this fine meal for us. Amen."

Leola's heart swelled. *And I thank You for my husband.*

The couple lingered over the meal. John Thomas shared his plans for hunting and fishing. "I can keep us in food, Leola. And first thing in the morning, I'll start clearing out the garden plot so we can plant us a garden. "Hit's a late start, but this be good river bottom land. We should git some harvest this year."

Leola agreed with all his plans but found it hard to focus on them. Her thoughts were on bedtime. When the meal was finally finished, they washed dishes together, pleased the hand pump brought ample water into the house.

With no other excuse to delay, Leola turned toward the bedroom. Unable to look at John Thomas, she spoke in a soft whisper. "I'd best get the bed made." She hoped the redness residing on her face was hidden in the dimly lit kitchen.

John Thomas nodded as he headed out the back door. "Reckon I'll go see if Lucy's settled in."

Leola savored some time alone. She found sheets and pillows from her trunk, then pulled out the quilt Ma gave her the night before the wedding.

"This here's your wedding quilt, Leola. It'll need mendin' over time. I reckon this quilt is jist like marriage. It'll need mendin' at times too. Find comfort in both of them, Leola."

Thank you, Ma. This is what I needed tonight. She made the bed, debating about whether to use the quilt since the hot June night still held much of the day's heat. She decided to fold the quilt across the end of the bed before she changed into her nightgown, another gift from Ma. Finally, Leola eased into bed, ready to find comfort in the arms of her husband.

Chapter Twenty-one

The rhythm of their first year of marriage matched the seasons. Leola sowed in spring, weeded all summer, then harvested her garden in the fall. Her days rarely changed. She rose at daybreak, started the coffee, then went outside to feed her chickens and gather eggs. Returning inside, she made breakfast and called John Thomas to come eat. The rest of the day she spent doing chores. If John Thomas wasn't night hunting, they sat together near the fireplace or rocking on the front porch, depending on the season.

Sundays became Leola's refuge, a day she looked forward to all week. The church wasn't far from the river road, close enough to walk; and when the winter weather made it impossible to walk, John Thomas hitched Lucy to the wagon.

After spending much of the week alone due to John Thomas's frequent trips to the woods, Leola's hunger for community grew. She wished she could say she was hungry for the preaching. The preacher delivered his sermons with fist pounding and yelling, seeming to enjoy fire and brimstone over the love and grace which was more to Leola's liking.

Loneliness had become Leola's constant companion, wrapping her like a tattered quilt which no longer held warmth. Taking a break from her chores, she wrote to Ma and her friends in Stringtown weekly, though she struggled to find things to say. Getting to the store to check the mail or post letters proved even more difficult, especially in the winter.

"Let's walk to the store. I'm needin' some tobaccy." Or "I'm hitchin' up Lucy. I need some feed. Thought you might be a mind to go."

Leola suspected it was more about her letters than tobacco or feed; still, John Thomas's understanding of her loneliness filled her with gratitude. Once the offer was made, she'd stop her chores to accompany him.

In September, Leola reckoned herself to be pregnant. Confirmed a few weeks later by a circuit-riding doctor, she and John Thomas were ecstatic. She spent her spare time sewing baby clothes and dreaming of a time when a child might finally help the loneliness let go of its unrelenting grip.

One cold Monday morning the next January, a wagon pulled up with a woman and two toddlers. The noisy sound of the wagon's wheels clambering over the dry, uneven ground brought John Thomas's hunting dog, Queenie, running from the back of the house while barking frantically.

Leola stood on the porch mesmerized, suppressing a laugh at the sight. A redheaded woman struggled to get the two little boys out of the wagon. The youngsters seemed to think it a game to run around the wagon bed rather than obey their ma. Finally grabbing each child by the hand, the visitor marched up the path with all the determination of a soldier marching to battle.

"Hello thar. Name's Eliza Monroe. This here's Delbert and Thelbert. They's twins. Don't ask me which be which, cain't tell half the time. I jist call 'Twin' and one of 'em comes a-runnin'." The mother's musical laugh made Leola's smile broader. "We jist moved here 'bout a month back. I heard at the store there be another young woman in these sites. So's I high-tailed it over even if 'hit's wash day. My 'poligies for that—jist couldn't wait a speck longer, I reckon."

Leola flew into action. A guest, and more important, a woman. "Please come out of the cold. We'll sit by the fire and have coffee." She spun around to Queenie before following her guest inside. "Stop that ruckus or I'll put you back in your pen."

She rushed to the kitchen to make coffee, stopping to gather the empty spools from her sewing basket. The twins might need something to play with. Returning to the front room, she found Eliza warming herself and the boys in front of the fireplace.

The next hour flew by as Leola and Eliza found enjoyment in each other's company. When the twins started fussing with each other, Eliza announced, "I'd best be a-goin'. Don't want to be wearin' out my welcome. 'Sides, these two'll be boxin' it out soon."

Leola saw the trio to the front porch with a promise to return the visit. Eliza turned halfway down the path. "If I'm seein' right, I'm thinkin' you got a little one coming 'bout summer. I know lots 'bout birthin' babies. My ma teached me. I'll be here for you, if you be wantin'."

Leola nodded, unable to express the gratitude welled up inside her. *Thank You, Lord, for sending me a friend, especially one with two children.* She hadn't realized until now that it wasn't just her family and friends she missed. She missed children.

She could hardly wait to tell John Thomas about the visit when he returned home from hunting. As soon as he shut the door behind him, he shared his own news.

"Leola, I met up with Henry Cochran in the woods this mornin'. He's a cousin jist home from the army. I reckon he likes huntin' and fishin' 'bout as much as me. He's sorely ready for a heap o' both after bein' gone for three years." John Thomas continued to rattle on about Henry, a rarity for him to be so talkative.

The shine in her husband's eyes brought another unexpected surprise. *How could I be so selfish? I didn't even notice; he's been as lonely as I have.* Leola decided to wait until tomorrow's breakfast to share her news.

Audrey Janet was born June 4, 1925. Eliza came to help with the birthing while John Thomas stayed outside with her husband and the twins. Leola labored from early morning into the evening. Sweat and exhaustion covered her body by the time the delivery was near.

"Come on, Leola," Eliza coached. "I reckon one more push and that thar baby'll be sayin' hello to the world."

With the next pain, a fatigued mother pushed hard, and the baby girl made her appearance. Eliza laid the baby on Leola's stomach. Silence filled the room.

When her ma had babies, they all cried as soon as they were born. Leola looked into Eliza's face and read the answer in her friend's tearful eyes.

Leola's wail brought John Thomas running into the room. "What's wrong, Leola?" She turned her head away from her husband, unable to speak. Coming closer to see the baby, he witnessed the reason for the mournful crying.

John Thomas and Leola's baby girl was buried the next day in the cemetery next to the church. The father and relatives gathered for the graveside service while Eliza stayed at Leola's bedside.

Leola spent the next week in bed letting only Eliza care for her. She longed for her mother but knew she wouldn't be coming. She'd just gotten a letter from Ma saying two of Leola's younger siblings had the measles.

When silent tears flowed down her face, she made no attempt to wipe them away, her hands too heavy to lift. When John Thomas entered the room, Leola turned away, unable to share her grief.

Four days after the birth, Eliza blew into the bedroom room like a March wind. "You hear me now, Leola. I knowd you got a broken heart, but 'hits time for you to git up out of that thar bed. You ain't helpin' yourself or John Thomas by layin' in this here bed."

Eliza's voice softened as she gently took Leola's face and turned it to her. "Reckon when hard times come, the Lord expects us to grab a holt of Him and keep on a-goin'. Find your faith, Leola, and He'll carry you through." She turned and opened the wardrobe next to the bed. "Let's git you a bath, then git on to cookin' up some supper for John Thomas. Ain't no tellin' what that poor man's been eatin' this week."

Soon Leola found herself sitting at the kitchen table peeling potatoes while Eliza cut pieces of pork to cook. Neither of them spoke, which Leola knew to be difficult for her chatty friend.

Leola finally broke the silence though she still couldn't look at her friend. "I reckon you're right, Eliza. I have to keep going. Thank you for all you've done since..." She stopped, unable to complete her sentence for fear of more tears.

When she spoke again strength and determination filled her voice. "I need to let John Thomas grieve with me. It's too heavy a burden to carry alone."

Eliza had gone by the time John Thomas returned home. He froze by the door seeing Leola rocking in the front room, the aroma of supper drifting from the kitchen. Hanging his hat on a peg near the door, he moved to her rocker and knelt on one knee. "'Hit's surely good to see you up, Leola. I feared you might..."

Leola looked into his eyes and gently covered his mouth. "Shh, I'm okay, just very sad." Her husband laid his head in her lap, crying softly while Leola stroked his hair.

After a few moments, Leola spoke again. "John Thomas, I been sitting here thinking. Maybe we should try to have another baby. I got a heap of baby clothes."

John Thomas lifted his head and gave his wife a teary smile. "I reckon that might be a right good idea, Leola."

The next day, a letter came from Ma. *Leola, honey, I know your heart hurts from losin' your sweet baby girl. Hold on, Daughter, God always gives sunshine after a rain.*

Leola and John Thomas moved through the late summer and fall with a special closeness grown out of their grief. On nice days, when the garden work was done, John Thomas would hitch Lucy to the wagon and take Leola for a ride. They would stop to pick the last of the wildflowers to put on Audrey Janet's grave, finding sweet comfort standing there, hands clasped together, hearts mending.

The fact that John Thomas seemed to be hunting and fishing less wasn't lost on Leola. She knew he'd need to get back to the woods and the river soon to help with their meals, but for now she relished the time her husband gave her.

The next January a letter came from Pa. Leola recognized Pa's handwriting at once. An icy chill ran through her body.

You're Ma's gone, Leola. She passed on quickly, not even time to git word to you about her sickness. She didn't want you to come when she was sick 'cause the snow be heavy here. Doc. Harvey says it was the consumption causin' her coughin' fer many months now. It be hard to think of her gone.

Grief again made its painful entrance into Leola's life. The letter hit the floor just before Leola's knees did. "John Thomaaas!"

He rushed into the front room and saw the paper in front of her. He read only the first few words before he lunged to the floor to hold his crying wife in his arms.

Dew lay on the grass in the early morning hours of September 23,1926 when John Thomas Cochran, Jr. arrived with a cry which swelled the hearts of his parents. Leola's joy knew no bounds as she cared for her baby boy.

"He's going to be a good baby, John Thomas. After the first howl, he's hardly been crying at all."

John Thomas looked at his son, then turned his eyes to the floor. Unsmiling, he whispered, "Reckon so, Leola."

By nightfall, the baby's small movements had stopped. He lay awake refusing to eat, as his chest heaved up and down. Leola held him closely, now willing him to cry. Before midnight, he was gone.

Once again, John Thomas, family and friends gathered beside a small open grave, saying their goodbyes to a baby boy who'd lived only nine hours.

Eliza again stayed with Leola, trying to ease her grief with little progress. Leola lay with her face turned to the wall, her thoughts on Ma and on her two babies.

Lord, where's my sunshine?

Chapter Twenty-Two

Cold air rushed against Leola's chest as she rocked on Eliza's front porch. Although glad the heat of summer had passed, she knew the coming weather would soon stop her morning visits with her friend. The two of them watched Eliza's twins play in the front yard. They sat silently for some time, unusual for the pair.

"Reckon you need to spill whatever's got your heart so burdened, Leola." Elisa never took her eyes off the kids.

Leola sighed. "Visiting two small graves is too much for John Thomas. It's like his time in the woods has become his lifeline. Our pain has become only his pain, so different from when we lost Audrey Janet." She looked at Eliza with tears in her eyes, swallowing a sob she didn't want to release.

Eliza took her friend's hand and pleaded, "Listen to me now, Leola. My bible tells me we can be pressed hard on every side, but not destroyed. Reckon you might be needin' more time on your knees, see iff'n the Lord cain't bring John Thomas back to you."

Leola nodded, ashamed to admit she hadn't been doing much kneeling lately.

Leola went to the cemetery often before the weather turned too cold to walk to her babies' graves. She put the tiny baby clothes in an old hat box, sure she'd never use them again. Without the comfort of her husband, Leola found herself drowning in the bleak days of fall.

A letter from Pa brought Leola some hope. She turned to John Thomas later in the evening as they sat by the fire. "John Thomas, I had a letter from Pa. He'd like us to come for Christmas. Do you think we could make the trip?"

For the first time in weeks, Leola's husband looked into her eyes. After a moment he responded. "I reckon we could, but we can only stay one night. I'll git Henry to feed the animals." He rose and put another log to the fire. "Course the weather will hafta be good."

Leola nodded without saying a word. She watched the fire sending out sparks from the addition of a new log. *Lord, we need a Christmas miracle. Help us to find each other again.*

Christmas Eve morning dawned with perfect traveling weather, cool and clear. They left at sunrise after a breakfast of cold biscuits and smoked ham. Once underway, Leola took in the sights of the winter forest. Holly and yaupon sprinkled the woods with bright splashes of red. The sage-green mistletoe hung like Christmas balls from the bare trees, a stark contrast to the evergreen pines. She breathed in the sweet smell of pine, grateful for the beautiful day and encouraged about the new year. There might not be any babies, but she could still make a good life with her husband.

"John Thomas, do you think the relatives will visit at Pa's today?" Leola hungered to see familiar faces.

She sighed when John Thomas merely shrugged his shoulders. Whether John Thomas enjoyed the visit or not, she intended to. *He can just sit in the corner alone and quiet for all I care!*

Being in her childhood home was difficult without Ma there, especially when Leola was in the kitchen. Every pot and utensil reminded her of the sweet times she worked alongside her mother cooking meal or canning vegetables.

The relatives stayed until late into the night visiting, singing, and eating the abundance of food brought by everyone. Being with Pa, her siblings, and the other relatives soothed Leola's hurting soul. She soaked it all in and tried not to think of returning to her empty home. For the first time in months she put her grief aside and found joy from those around her.

Christmas morning brought another day of perfect weather—blue skies and a warmer than usual temperature. After a large breakfast, Leola set about cleaning the dishes when John Thomas reached for his hat.

"Think I'll go feed Lucy," he said as he moved toward the front door.

"Wait a minute, Son." Leola's father motioned to the chair next to him in the front room. "I'd like to talk with you for a minute."

Leola slowly dried the dish in her hand, listening to her father's words. *I shouldn't listen, but something has to change in our marriage. I think Pa knows this.*

"Ain't no shame to grieve, John Thomas. Lord knows I did my share of it when Leola's ma died. But a man has to be strong, believin' God's got a plan even in times of trouble. It's breaking Leola's heart to see you turned away from her." Pa kept his eyes on his son-in-law, the words hanging in the air like a balloon.

Several moments passed. John Thomas started to leave then stopped, his back to his father-in-law and said, "I'll be a-thinkin' on your words. And I thank ya kindly."

When he stepped out the door, Leola left the kitchen to stand beside her father. Together they watched John Thomas's slumped shoulders as he crossed the yard and headed toward the woods, apparently forgetting about his plans to feed the mule.

"Thank you for trying, but he's so stubborn, I don't know if he'll…" Leola's voice choked with tears. She couldn't finish her words.

Pa put his arm around his daughter's shoulders. "You got to believe, Leola. Iff'n God helped bring down that wall around the city of Jericho, I reckon He can bring down the wall around John Thomas."

Leola and John Thomas left after the noon meal

in order to be home before dark. Once in the wagon, John Thomas turned to his wife. "I reckon there be time to visit your ma's grave if you've a mind to."

"Oh, John Thomas, could we? I've been thinking about Ma all morning. Thank you for offering."

Lucy made it to the cemetery in short time and John Thomas helped Leola down from the wagon. When they found Ma's grave, John Thomas hung back, giving Leola a chance to be alone at the gravesite.

Leola stared down at Ma's headstone, a familiar ache squeezed at her chest. A soft whisper came from her lips. "Life's harder than I thought it would ever be, Ma. I need you so badly." As she stood, tears falling on the ground, the hurt began to lessen. Soon, a half-smile played on her lips. "Thanks, Ma. I love you, too." Leola stepped back from the grave and faced her husband. "I think we'd better be going now. Thank you for giving me this time, John Thomas."

John Thomas hesitated, then reached for Leola's hand. "I be needin' to ask forgiveness from you, Leola. I left you alone in my grief over our second baby. I reckon it be the wrong thing for a man to do to his wife. If you'll let me, I'll be sharin' our grief and seein' if we cain't git past it."

Heartbeats flew through Leola's body, making her knees weak. Love and gratefulness overflowed in her like a hard rain gushes from an upturned bucket. "I think it would be fine, John Thomas. We both need to find a way past our grief."

Wilbur Martin was born October 23, 1927. His parents treated him like a fragile teacup for the first few weeks. Gradually, their fears of losing another baby declined as the baby boy grew. John Thomas returned to hunting and fishing with his cousin. He spent long hours away from home, leaving Leola and his baby son hours on end.

For the next six months Leola took care of their son and tried to make do with the dwindling pantry. One morning, when John Thomas slept late after a long night in the woods, Leola set cold biscuits and congealed grits in front of him, not willing to serve a hot breakfast.

"John Thomas, I don't hold with laziness. We've got a child to care for now and the tab at Frank's store is getting high. He's surely going to want to be paid soon. Eliza told me they're hiring at the mill. I'd be obliged if you'd try to get a job cutting trees."

John Thomas took a quick glance at his pitiful offering for breakfast. Without a word, he retrieved his hat from the peg by the front door and quietly disappeared out the door.

"Surely there's not a more stubborn man alive!" She picked up his plate, loudly scraping the food into the slop bucket. "At least the pigs'll eat good today!" Then she opened the pantry, mentally taking note of how long the flour, sugar, coffee, and cornmeal would last.

John Thomas returned mid-morning, finding Leola rocking their son on the front porch. He stood in the yard, holding the tattered hat in his hands. "Thought about what you said, Leola. Made sense. I headed over to the mill and hired on. I start tomorra." Returning the hat to his head, he continued, "Reckon I'll go fix the chicken coop. Saw some fox tracks the last couple mornings. Thinkin' I might not git another chance to work on it."

Leola watched his back retreat as he headed to the chicken pens. Breath escaped her lungs for the first time since he'd returned. She planned the cake she'd make when the first paycheck arrived.

A sweet harmony fell over their home. John Thomas labored cutting trees for the mill. Soon, Leola paid the tab at Frank's store and began stocking their pantry with staples. She made a cake for John Thomas on his first payday and continued to do so every payday following.

Another son, Vernon Earl, arrived on December 27, 1929. The same year, the nation fell headlong into a depression. Leola laughed one day when she read the nation's new motto in the newspaper: Wear it out, use it up, make it do or do without. *We've been doing that for years already.* Now more than ever, she was grateful for John Thomas's job at the sawmill.

While the Great Depression created unthinkable conditions for thousands of Americans, families around the river road saw no breadlines, no men holding signs asking for work, no children going door to door begging for table scraps. Here in the deep piney woods of western Louisiana, where most of their existence came from hunting, fishing and gardening, the Depression existed only as something to be read about in the newspaper.

In June of 1932, John Thomas and Leola were

blessed with a baby girl, Doris Lucille. Leola was beside herself with joy as she envisioned having the same relationship with her daughter as she'd had with her Ma. Two-year-old Vernon struggled to call his new sister "Doris." It came out sounding like "Dawfie." The name stuck and soon all the family were calling the sweet baby girl Dawfie.

The long fingers of the Depression came close to home in 1933 when John Thomas lost his job at the mill. "I know'd it was comin', Leola. Nobody's buildin' so there ain't no need for lumber. I reckon I'll be doin' more fishin' and huntin' now."

The couple, now with three children to feed and clothe, struggled to make ends meet. Leola squeezed everything she could out of her garden that year, grateful the rain had lasted through July and they had a plentiful harvest. Sadly, the cow given to them as a wedding gift died the next year. With no money to purchase another, they no longer had milk. Leola used water to make biscuits for breakfast and cornpones for supper. She learned to ration the coffee by adding just a teaspoon of fresh coffee to the used coffee grounds to help the flavor.

John Thomas spent every day in the woods with his cousin Henry. Usually he came home with catfish or some squirrels for their supper. If not, Leola fried some salt pork, boiled a few potatoes, and opened a jar of canned tomatoes. She tried not to resent the time John Thomas spent in the woods; still, it became the cause of several arguments between them.

"Lord 'o mercy, woman. I've got to feed the family. There's lots of huntin' going on in these here woods now.

Henry and I have to walk farther and farther to find kill. You gotta let me keep at it!"

A blistering July sun beat down on Leola's back as she bent to weed the garden. Most of the summer of 1935 had been without the nurturing rain her garden needed. If it didn't rain by the end of the week, she and the boys would be watering each plant from lard buckets filled with water from the well.

Leola glanced over at her kids playing in the yard inside the fence. She often had the brothers watch their sister while she did the chores. Today, the boys sat on the grass to roll a ball back and forth between them, the oppressive morning heat keeping them from more active play.

Three-year old Dawfie finally started walking just a few months ago, but seemed to prefer sitting in her tiny rocking chair playing with her trinkets. A familiar worry moved through Leola, slow as a June bug crossing the porch. *I'm thanking You, Lord, for her walking. Now if You could just let me hear some words from her mouth.*

Noise from the river road made Leola turn from her children to see the preacher on horseback coming toward the garden.

"Howdy, Leola." The man removed his big, black hat then took a red bandana from his coat pocket to wipe his brow.

"Howdy, Preacher. Hot day to be out riding." Leola knew what was coming. The same thing the preacher brought up each time he spoke to her.

"The Lord ordains the heat and the cold, Leola. No reason to stop His work." His stern face made it clear he was there on business. "John Thomas around? Thought I'd visit with him before making my calls to the sick."

"John Thomas is fishing today, Preacher."

"Seems he's fishing or hunting every day lately. Even on the Lord's day." He twisted his head to the direction of the kids. After a moment, he turned back to Leola. "Dawfie talking yet?"

"Not yet, Preacher. But she's walking now." Leola worked to keep a smile.

The preacher hesitated, taking his time to wipe his brow again and returning the hat to his head. "Well, tell John Thomas I'll be looking for him come Sunday. Needs to get himself straight with the Lord for his family's sake."

Heat hotter than the air around her welled up in Leola as she managed a tight-lipped goodbye. She attacked her weeds with renewed vigor. *Preacher should be doing some of his own weed pulling. There's plenty of them in his pews every Sunday!*

Chapter Twenty-three

The Great Depression held the country in its grips for six years. Leola and John Thomas sought out news from the few neighbors who owned a radio and from the newspapers loaned by the owner of the store. Some days the depression seemed far away; other times, in their struggle to make do or do without, the full weight of a failing economy pressed on their shoulders.

By the fall of 1935, President Franklin D. Roosevelt's New Deal—a plan to put people back to work and boost the economy—began to show positive results. Called the Alphabet Agencies, the CCC, TVA, and WPA created much-welcomed jobs across the country.

Leola and John Thomas often spent their evenings discussing the happenings around the country. "That President Roosevelt's a smart man. Reckon he'll git us back on our feet," John Thomas commented late one night.

Leola sighed as she sewed more patches on

the boys' thread-bare pants, not sure whose feet the president was helping.

One sultry August day Leola fanned herself as she rocked on Eliza's porch. "I'll be glad when summer lets go this year. This heat has us snapping at each other. The boys are good to help with chores, but they fuss when I ask them to watch Dawfie. I'm afraid she'll wander off," she said as she watched the boys play with Eliza's twins.

"I'm worried, Eliza. Dawfie's like a caterpillar wrapped up in a cocoon. I'm just waiting for the butterfly to come out."

Eliza glanced at Dawfie, who sat rocking her body back and forth on her perch of the porch step, concentrating on the small resin doll in her hands. "Seems to me 'hits like her body's movin' on but her mind jest ain't catched up yet. I reckon she'll catch up in time, Leola."

Leola loved her friend for wanting to ease her worries, but at age three Dawfie did few things her boys did at the same age. *Lord, help me know what to do for this child. I want to do my best by her.* Talking to the Lord about Dawfie comforted her but all too soon, worry and fear returned to make Leola feel like her feet were stuck in the red mud of the river road. She had the sensation of sinking with no plan for getting unstuck.

"John Thomas, I need you to go to the store to get

some cornmeal. I can't make cornpones for supper until I get some more." Leola reached to the top shelf over the cabinet and pulled down an old coffee can. She shook it until her fingers found a dime in its dark cavern. "Just get ten cents' worth. Can's almost empty."

"A'right then," John Thomas said as he headed out the door.

Leola knew he'd hoped to go fishing on the shady, cool banks of the river. She didn't blame him for wanting to get to a cooler place. The sweltering August heat had already hit the early morning.

"You kids get on outside. Boys, watch your sister. I'll be out as soon as I finish the dishes." She filled a basin with the hot water simmering on the stove during their meal, added a few soap flakes, and plunged the dishes into the soapy water. Her hands moved into automatic mode, her mind not on the task at hand.

Leola's gaze returned to the blue and gold Seaport coffee can on the shelf above the counter. Thoughts swirled through her head as she tried to think of ways to fill the can with much needed funds. Her hens were only providing enough eggs for the family. With no milk cow, she couldn't sell off extra milk. A scripture from the previous Sunday's sermon popped into her head. "Be careful of nothing; but in everything by prayer and supplication with thanksgiving let your requests be made known unto God. And the peace of God, which passes all understanding, will keep your hearts and minds through Christ Jesus…" A peace came over her, making her smile as she hummed her favorite gospel.

She spent the next few hours working in the garden, picking the last few tomatoes and harvesting a bunch of mustard greens for supper. Midmorning, she hustled the kids inside.

"It's getting too hot to stay out any longer. You boys go in and read your books. Dawfie, come with Mama. You can play on the kitchen floor while I start lunch." Leola smiled as she watched her boys hustle for the door. They loved books as much as she did at their age, even though they'd read their few books many times over.

Leola looked up from where she was washing mustard greens to see John Thomas headed toward the house.

"Got news, Leola," he said as soon as he walked into the kitchen. "Met me a man at the store. Name's Bill McNair. Says he's from Chicago. He takes heirloom portraits. He's a-comin' here next Saturday to take us a family portrait." He beamed like he had the best news since the end of the Great War.

Leola turned and put wet hands on her hips. "John Thomas, have you forgotten we're in the middle of a depression? We don't have two nickels to rub together!" Her hands were dripping water onto the floor, but she didn't care. "How do you know this Bill McNair's not a con man? I read about plenty of them in this depression, trying to take what little money a person has. You just tell him when he comes—if he comes—you changed your mind!"

John Thomas grabbed his hat and fishing pole. As he walked out the door, he said in a low, steady voice.

"I already paid him half with my tobaccy money. Plan on havin' the rest by time he comes. You'd best make sure our good clothes are ready fer next Saturday."

Leola stomped one foot and slapped both hands back into the sink of mustard greens with such a force water splashed her in the face. "We'll see about that!"

At supper, John Thomas and Leola refused to recognize each other. The boys shot quick glances between their parents, silently questioning the mood in the kitchen. At the end of the meal, John Thomas spoke. "You boys go on outside and catch yourself some lightning bugs. I be needin' to talk to your ma."

The boys grabbed two old mason jars and headed out the door with a slam. John Thomas's determined face told Leola he hadn't changed his mind about the portrait. She steeled herself for another confrontation.

"Had me another piece of news today, Leola. I took off 'fore I give it. Saw a notice at the store. The mill's running part-time agin. The WPA is building roads, schools, bridges, and the like all over the country. There be a need for lumber agin. Went on over and got hired on three days a week startin' this Monday. I'll have me a paycheck by Wednesday. Reckon some of 'hit will pay the rest I owe the man from Chicago."

He stared hard at Leola. "I still mean to get the portrait, Leola." Seeing the frown on his wife's face, he wiped his brow with the back of his hand and continued in a softer voice, "I never got no pictures of my ma and pa. Reckon I mean to have this done for my own kids to have someday." He pushed back his chair and stood. "Fixin' to go see how many lightning bugs those young'uns catched."

Leola stared at her empty plate. A part of her softened at what John Thomas said, but then she remembered winter was coming on and all three kids needed new shoes. Whatever speck of kindness her husband's speech brought on hardened like a rock. "All right, John Thomas. I reckon I'll do it. But I sure don't have to like it!"

Relations remained strained between the couple all week and the boys reacted by being grumpy and whiney. Waking up early Saturday morning, Leola welcomed the day eager to get the portrait over.

By midmorning, the family sat on the front porch dressed in their Sunday best. Twice already, John Thomas reprimanded the boys not to get their clothes dirty. "I ain't tellin' you boys ag'in to be still. Next, I'll be huntin' for a switch!

Sorry her sons were forced to stay still, Leola opened her mouth to suggest the man might not be coming, when they saw a small car on the road and heard a yell. "Hello, are you the Cochrans?"

John Thomas shot out of his chair. "Shore be! Come on over, Bill."

Well, I'll be. He did show up. Leola followed her husband to the front gate.

The next few minutes were a blur of confusion as the photographer set up his equipment, then struggled to get the family arranged in a way to fit in the camera's frame. Leola bit her tongue more than once. *He's far too picky for my liking.*

Finally, Bill had the little family in a pose with John Thomas on one end and Leola on the other. The boys were standing between them and Dawfie sat in her small rocker.

"Hold it there, Cochrans," the photographer yelled from the back of his equipment. Before the camera clicked and a puff of black smoke rose above Bill's head, Leola made a quick turn away from the camera.

No one noticed Leola's move, but realizing she'd ruined the picture made her stomach turn sick. *What have I done?* Avoiding the eyes of both men, Leola mumbled goodbye to the photographer and hustled the kids inside to change from their Sunday clothes. John Thomas stayed behind to pay the man and chat about the Depression.

When the kids were changed, Leola shooed them out to play. She headed into the kitchen to start lunch, her mind churning. In the end, she'd defied her husband, still determined to make her disagreement known. Leola turned into her bedroom, lunch forgotten. She silently moved to her knees. "Lord, I've done a bad thing. I'm so ashamed of myself. Help me make it up to my John Thomas."

Chapter Twenty-four

Fall finally arrived, but the cool weather did little to help the shame burning within Leola. Yet her determination to tell John Thomas what she had done lost steam each time she tried. Excuses ranged from *I'm too busy to get into it now* to *John Thomas is in such a good mood, no need to spoil it*. When alone while hanging laundry or gathering eggs, she remembered with a twang of guilt. "I must tell him before the portrait arrives."

Weeks passed and Leola had yet to tell John Thomas about her actions. By December, Leola convinced herself the man from Chicago was a con man. "I don't see a need to tell John Thomas now," she confided to her chickens one morning. The relief she expected from her decision never came.

Christmas fell mid-week, which made it impossible to make the trip to Texas as John Thomas had only Christmas Day off. "Just as well," he told Leola.

"The weather's far too bad to be a-travelin'."

Leola agreed but something kept pulling her to see Pa. The last letter from one of her sisters informed her their father had been "feelin' poorly." An uneasiness settled over her each time she thought of her father.

The week after Christmas, John Thomas came home from a trip to Frank's store. "Leola, honey, your sister called jist when I got to the store. Your Pa died in his sleep last night."

Leola nodded and turned back to the stove where she was preparing lunch. "Reckon I knew it was coming. I've been feeling troubled about him ever since the last letter came." Her tears sizzled as they hit the hot stove.

John Thomas walked over and took the large wooden spoon from her hand. "I can git this meal ready for the kids."

Leola nodded and moved toward the bedroom. She stopped at the door. "John Thomas..."

"No, Leola," John Thomas interrupted. "The funeral's tomorrow and I cain't risk missin' work and losin' my job. Besides the sky's lookin' like another storm may be movin' in soon." He put the spoon down, walked to her, and put his hands on her shoulders. "I'm sorry, Leola. He were a good man. Iff'n you feel like it this afternoon, I'll take you to the store so you can call yer sister."

She nodded again and closed the bedroom door to mourn the father she had loved dearly and who had taught her so much about life.

The harsh weather continued through January, doing little to soothe the grief Leola carried. Several days the boys were unable to attend school when ice or snow kept the school bus from coming down the river road. Those days, forced to stay inside with three kids, Leola's nerves were frazzled by the time John Thomas returned from work.

Too often John Thomas announced his plan to go night hunting. Since the death of her father, fear of another loss rose up in Leola each time he left the house to hunt in the dark, cold woods.

"Why don't you wait for another night, John Thomas? The rain from earlier today might return," she'd plead; or, "I think we still have plenty of the last hog you killed. I reckon it can wait awhile before you kill another."

Maybe John Thomas didn't hear her over the chatter of the boys or maybe he just refused to answer. Each time he silently reached for his hat and gun, giving his customary "Night, kids" and "Don't be a'waitin' up, Leola."

But she did wait up, relieved to hear the door latch jingle. She lay silent in the bed pretending to be asleep as John Thomas slipped in beside her, thankful he was home safe. Yet, sleep still eluded her as images of what could have happened flashed through her mind.

One Monday in late February, another round of freezing rain kept the boys home from school. Frustrated, Leola struggled to find places to hang the wash inside the front room.

"Boys, y'all need to stay put on the floor with

your toys. I need to get this wet laundry dry by the time your daddy comes home." She didn't include Dawfie in the reprimand. Her youngest would sit in her small chair near the fire all day, rocking and holding one of her baby dolls.

A sigh escaped Leola. She didn't have time to worry about Dawfie now. With only minimal changes of clothes for the family, it was time to get some clean ones ready to wear.

By late afternoon, the dry laundry lay folded in the basket ready for an ironing the next day. Supper simmered on the stove and the boys retreated to their bedroom to read from their books. Leola placed another log on the fire and sat in her rocker next to Dawfie. As quiet surrounded her in a rare moment of solitude, she thought of her Pa.

Suddenly something he said to her long ago filled Leola's thoughts. "Always be truthful in this life, Daughter. If you've wronged someone, they may not forgive you, but God surely will." In this moment, she understood why she'd found no peace these many months. She'd been untruthful to her husband. For the first time since that hot August day, she asked God to forgive her and to help her find the courage to tell John Thomas.

When the children were asleep and she and John Thomas sat before the fire later in the evening, she planned to tell John Thomas about what she'd done the day the portrait was taken. Whatever his reaction, she knew it wouldn't be as bad as keeping it from him all these months. *Whether the portrait ever arrives or not, I must make things right with my husband.*

The rain stopped by the time John Thomas walked home from the mill, though not soon enough to prevent him getting soaked on his walk home. Leola gabbed some clothes from her ironing basket. “Here’s some dry clothes. They’re not ironed but they’re better than those wet things you have on now.”

All through supper, Leola thought of the conversation she’d have later in front of the fire. Her hands trembled as she planned how to word her confession to John Thomas. At the end of the meal, she shooed the boys off to get ready for bed. “John Thomas, would you get Dawfie ready for bed while I clean the dishes?”

“Reckon I’ll go huntin’ now the rain’s let up. Should be a full moon iff’n the clouds break.”

Leola’s shoulders slumped slightly. “It’s terribly cold and everything is covered in ice. You think it’s a good night to be hunting?”

For once, John Thomas responded to his wife’s plea. “Cain’t be missing a full moon, Leola. Henry’s likely waitin’ at the river by now.”

“When do you think you’ll be back? Should I keep the coffee hot?”

He sighed, glanced down at his feet, then back at his wife. “I’ll be back by and by, I reckon.”

Leola watched from the window as John Thomas pushed his hat low on his head and turned up the collar of his coat before turning to the path leading to the woods. A quick whistle brought Queenie to his side.

An icy chill having nothing to do with the freezing

temperatures filled Leola's body. A strong love and even stronger disappointment surged through her. "Oh, John Thomas. When will I ever get a chance to bare my heart to you? Please come home safely."

The night crawled slowly. Leola spent the hours alternating between standing at the window staring into the moonlit night and sitting by the fire. Her mind flooded with memories. Unlike recent nights when she sat alone in the front room with a heart full of resentment, these memories were of the sweet times when she felt John Thomas's love. *Lord, please let the sky clear so John Thomas's hunt will be over soon.* She repeated her petition over and over long into the night.

Leola jerked when she heard the ping of freezing rain on the tin roof. "Surely those crazy men are headed home now." She moved the lamp beside her chair to the front window to intently search for any sign of the hunters.

After only a moment, she saw Henry walking with one arm around John Thomas, carrying most of his weight. Leola threw open the door and raced onto the porch, never stopping to grab a coat. The coldness sucked the air out of her lungs. By the time she could speak, Henry had reached the porch.

"Get a bed ready, Leola. We were headed home when the rain took us. We'll talk when we get John Thomas in dry clothes and settled in bed."

"What happened, Henry? Is it bad?"

"Not bad yet but it could be iff'n we don't git him dry," Henry spoke sternly.

She flew into action, pulling back covers and

grabbing dry clothes in the same movement. She left Henry to do the job of getting wet clothes off a man who could do little to help.

Prayers flew from her lips as she stood trembling by the fire. *"Lord, I'm asking You right now to spare John Thomas. I know full well what can happen when someone gets wet in weather like this. I can't bear another passing, especially not my John Thomas."* A touch on her shoulder caused her to spin around, fear stealing her heartbeats.

Henry's pants were wet from the knees down and his lips trembled. "He's restin' now, Leola. I won't be a'lyin' to you, hit's not good. He slipped when we got to the river and fell in. Queenie went in after him and got swept away by the swift waters. I grabbed him from the bank, but I think he swallowed plenty a'water into his lungs. Got him here as fast as I could."

Chapter Twenty-five

By morning, John Thomas had a fever, which grew steadily higher as the day wore on. Leola sent Henry for the doctor, with the children to drop off at Eliza's on the way. She knew her friend would start praying as soon as she heard the news.

The doctor took his time examining John Thomas then turned to Leola. "It's his lungs, Leola. It could get worse over the next few days. You'd best rest when you can. If this blasted weather will break, I'll ask my wife to come give you a hand."

But Leola refused to leave John Thomas's side. She worked relentlessly, ensuring he was warm, putting cool cloths on his feverish brow, and trying to get him to swallow some broth. No amount of persuasion from Henry or the doctor's wife could get her to rest. Intent on caring for him, she had no words for anyone. When alone in the room with her husband, she begged God to let him live.

In the middle of the second night, John Thomas's eyes opened, found Leola's face above his and with a struggle said, "By and by, I reckon." A spasm of racking coughs followed, then came a fitful sleep.

When the doctor arrived on Friday morning, four days after the hunting trip, he found John Thomas in a much-weakened state and Leola near exhaustion. "It's in God's hands now, Leola."

Leola frantically shook her head. Not yet. It couldn't be. "John Thomas, wake up. I have something to tell you." She repeated the phrase over and over, hardly able to stand any longer.

The doctor gently pushed her into the nearby chair, carefully taking the wet cloth from her hand. "Sit here if you must stay, Leola. He can't hear what you're saying but he might know you're holding his hand. I'll come back later this afternoon."

When the doctor returned, John Thomas's breathing was more labored. He shook his head in response to Leola's questioning eyes. A loud, low rattle came from John Thomas, followed by silence.

Leola jerked back to her husband. He was gone. In one movement she shoved her chair away from the bed, falling to her knees. "No, John Thomas. You can't leave me," she keened. Great cries rose and fell from her body with a strength which belied the weariness in her bones.

The doctor waited for the wails to pass. Finally, spent from the outpour of emotion, Leola rose and quietly spoke. "Doc, please ask your wife to bring me water and clothes. I must prepare my husband's body."

The next day most of the community arrived for John Thomas's visitation. The bedroom door, which once closed out the world and held the couple's own private happiness, now lay across two sawhorses in the front room. A roughly made pine box holding John Thomas's body rested on the door.

Leola sat near the head of the casket, accepting words of kindness from family and friends. Her thank-you's were scarcely above a whisper. The women gathered in the room quietly chatting. Outside, the weather had cleared, and men stood around a big fire in the yard while children played nearby.

When Eliza arrived with Leola's children, she held them close, then sent the boys out to play with their cousins. Dawfie went to her chair by the fire, unaffected by the surroundings. As the number of women in the room grew, so did the noise. Leola welcomed the sound, letting it drown out her own thoughts.

Finally, she asked for the preacher. "Preacher, I'm asking you now to be kind when you speak final words over John Thomas. He preached his own funeral while alive with how he treated his family and others in this community. I don't think he'll be needing a lot of words from you." She paused, lost in thought, then added, "And I'd like to hear *Sweet By and By* sung at the funeral." She turned away from the preacher then, not willing to hear anything he might want to say.

She found her friend. "Eliza, you've been a good friend, taking the kids and all. I need to ask you to take them a little while longer. I need to do my grieving."

For the next few days, Leola stayed home alone, taking food brought to her door and dismissing any attempt to visit. "I'm thanking you," she said softly then closed the door. Eliza came every day and received the same treatment.

Three days after John Thomas's funeral, Eliza refused to let Leola shut her out. "Leola, you ain't never gonna know God's grace for a time like this iff'n you don't get out of this house. Hit's time to start livin' agin."

"I'm alone, Eliza. How can I live without my John Thomas?" Leola's eyes filled with tears. *How many tears can one body shed in a single lifetime?*

"What makes you think you're alone? Don't you know John Thomas will be by your side fer the rest o' your natural life? And what about God? You know He cares for the sparrow? I reckon He can care for you and John Thomas's young'uns. And you won't be raising your kids alone. Plenty of us around here to help."

Slowly the words found their mark. An overwhelming rush of resolve filled Leola. The strength which moved her from Texas to Louisiana had taken root with every death, every cornpone made with water, every lonely night before the fire. The acorn had become a tree, ready to let its roots hold strong regardless of future storms.

Tears streamed down her cheeks as she grabbed her coat. "Let's go get my kids. I'll need to start their supper soon."

Chapter Twenty-six

The aroma of strong coffee and bacon frying on the stove woke Leola with a start. She sat up in bed and glanced out the bedroom window. The darkness told her sunrise wouldn't arrive for many hours. *Why's John Thomas up this early? It's hours before he leaves for work.*

The smell disappeared as quickly as it came. Disoriented from her dream, she lay back down and pulled the covers tightly around her chin. *Will the pain ever stop?* A fitful sleep followed, filled with scenes of the terrifying days of John Thomas's illness.

"Mama, we're hungry. Why are you still sleepin'?" Leola's two boys were standing by her bed, poking on the quilt she lay under.

"I'm getting up, boys. Don't wake up Dawfie yet. I'll get the fire going." *Seems like everything is off kilter since John Thomas passed. Hard as I try, I can't seem to get back on track.* Leola hurried to gather the eggs, disappointed to find her hens had laid only two. She returned to the kitchen to make a breakfast of grits, bacon, and hot biscuits. Leola thanked God once more for the kindness of her neighbors who had shown up frequently with offers of food.

"I kilt me another hog this week, Ms. Leola. I surely don't have room for any more meat. Hit's already smoked, ready to eat. I'd be appreciative iff'n you'd take it off my hands." Or, "My boys found a big crop of mayhaws. It made too much jelly for just us. Thought you might like a few jars." Several times, she found flour, corn meal, and coffee on her front porch left quietly by a kind neighbor.

The boys were soon fed and off to school. Dawfie sat by the fire while Leola washed the breakfast dishes. A noise pulled her attention to the window over her sink. Her eyes filled with tears when she saw Henry attaching a plow to his mule, preparing to turn over the moist March soil in her garden. He'd been around often since John Thomas's death, cleaning out the mule's stall and chopping firewood. Once he repaired the fence around the house after a storm blew a section of it down.

Leola stopped asking him in for a cup of coffee after getting the same reply several times. "No thank ya, best be gittin' on." She'd watch him replace his battered hat, reminding her of the many times she watched John Thomas do the same. The few times he looked directly at her; she recognized the pain of grief in his eyes. It somehow comforted her, knowing someone else missed her husband.

The sound of a wagon pulling up to her fence brought Leola out of the of the boy's room where she worked at changing bed sheets. "Hello, Eliza. I'm surprised to see you here in the middle of the day."

"I'm makin' a delivery, Leola. Been to Frank's store. You had a package delivered yesterdey. Postmark says Chicago. Thought I'd bring it by."

Leola's breath caught in her throat and her knees weakened as she struggled to focus on her friend. *The portrait. It's really here. It wasn't a con. Oh, John Thomas, how I wish I'd trusted the man the way you did. Wish I'd trusted you.*

"Leola, honey, do you want me to stay while you open it?" Eliza repeated her question.

Finding her voice, Leola responded in a low voice, "No, but I thank you for offering. Dawfie's napping. Reckon I'll open it alone."

Eliza handed her a wrapped package from the wagon seat. "A'right then, I'll be on my way. Come see me soon, Leola."

Nodding, Leola hugged the package to her chest as she watched Eliza move the wagon out to the river road, bouncing over the large muddy ruts caused by the April rains. She returned to her porch to sit in the rocker close to the door in case Dawfie woke up. Placing the parcel in her lap, Leola stared at it for several minutes as memories flooded her mind, making her eyes glisten with tears.

Finally, she slowly unwrapped the package,

gasping when she saw the portrait of her family. The tears which had threatened to spill now slid down her cheeks as she stared at every detail of the portrait. John Thomas first, standing tall and straight, then the kids, so cute in their dress clothes. Last, she looked at herself. There she stood facing away from the camera.

"Oh, John Thomas, you were so excited to have this portrait taken and I spoiled it. Please forgive me." The familiar peace which had sustained her since her husband's death filled her once again. She rose from the rocker, ready to face this day and the days to come.

Chapter Twenty-seven

Most of the time poverty lays over you like an unwelcome coat; other times it squeezes like a pair of pants two sizes too small. On one such occasion, we lived in a small apartment in a row of attached apartments, four in all. To say the walls were thin would be an understatement. We heard most of the family life on each side of us.

Mother stood at the stove making our nightly staple of fried potatoes when she heard a noise out the back door. Opening the door to investigate, she discovered the four children from next door eating the potato peels she had earlier dumped into the trash can.

She closed the door, knowing she didn't have enough fried potatoes to share. It was one of the few times I saw my mother cry.

Leola sat on the front porch listening to the early

morning sound of a woodpecker's sharp hits on tree bark, and the thump made when a squirrel scampered from one tree to the next. Knowing these sounds would soon be drowned out by two noisy boys, she savored the solitude of the early June morning. Against her will, her mind drifted to the thought nagging her for days: the empty Seaport coffee can on the shelf in the kitchen.

Without John Thomas's paycheck and the meat and fish he so abundantly provided, Leola was thrown into a kind of poverty she'd never known before. She couldn't rely on family and neighbors forever; she had to find a way to make up those lost resources. She needed a plan. Bowing her head, she asked God to give one to her.

Later in the morning, Leola sat lowering the hem on one of Dawfie's dresses. Quiet as a floating cloud, a plan came to mind. It played around in her mind as she weighed the pros and cons. A scripture hit her thoughts so strongly she looked around to see if someone had joined her. *Cast your cares on Him, He will care for you.* "Okay, Lord. I'll do it believing You'll provide the means."

"Boys, get your sister. We're going to visit Eliza." Leola left the dress in the rocker as she rushed to get the wagon hitched to her mule. Thoughts of her plan flew through her head faster than she could process them.

In short time, she sat on Eliza's front porch, Dawfie perched in her lap while the boys played chase in the yard with Eliza's twins.

"Might as well spell the beans, Leola. I can always tell iff'n you got something on yer mind," her friend said as she sat cutting eyes from potatoes soon to be planted.

"I reckon I'm just a little scared to say what I'm thinking for fear you'd think I'm crazy."

"I know'd you for years now, Leola, and I cain't rightly say I ever heard you talkin' crazy. What's on yer mind?"

"I need to find a way to make a living since John Thomas is gone. I've got Ma's sewing machine and I'm not bad at making clothes. I'm thinking I might could sew for people in the community," Leola said, the words spilling quickly out of her mouth. "What do you think, Eliza?"

Eliza's hand stopped working on the potatoes long enough for her to turn to her friend. "I reckon that's a fine idea, Leola. I'd be yer first customer. The boys need new shirts and pants and I'm surely findin' it hard to do ever'thin' by myself. I git tired real fast now with another young'un comin' this Christmas."

Forgetting her plan, Leola reached to squeeze her friend's arm. "Oh, Eliza. I'm so glad! Maybe this one will be a girl."

"I'd love a daughter I could talk with, do things... Oh, I'm sorry, Leola. I didn't think..."

"It's okay. I understand. It's one of the reasons I want to make some money. I've a mind to take Dawfie to a specialist in Lake Charles. I need to know more about her than what Doc is telling me."

Leola paused, then shared the rest of her thoughts. "My house is closest to the river. I'm thinking when hog killing time comes this winter, I can offer my place to do the butchering. John Thomas set up a good butchering place behind the animal stalls, and I can keep plenty of hot coffee going and maybe even offer some teacakes. All I'd ask for is a portion of the meat." She threw an apprehensive glance at Eliza.

"Why, Leola Cochran, I never know'd what a bid'ness woman you are!"

Leola blushed, pleased Eliza approved of her plan. She felt better than she had in weeks just knowing she might have a way to provide for herself and the children. "Now I just need the Lord to send me some customers."

"Oh, don't you be worryin' 'bout that. Between my mouth and our God, you'll have plenty of customers."

Chapter Twenty-eight

In the months to come, Leola marveled at God's provision. She spent long hours at her sewing machine making dresses, pants and shirts for those in the community. When winter brought freezing temperatures, she served steaming coffee and teacakes to hunters who came to butcher their hog meat. She never knew if they came because it was more convenient than doing it at their own homes or because they were helping out a widow. Regardless, it provided her with meat to feed her children, making her grateful at the end of every butchering day.

Dawfie was four years old when Leola finally had enough money to make a trip to Lake Charles to see a doctor who specialized in children. Doc told Leola that Dawfie's problem was from her thyroid and she'd grow out of it. Unwilling to wait any longer, Leola wanted an answer for Dawfie's lack of speech and limited interaction with others.

She asked John Thomas's Uncle Carl, who had just bought a 1928 Ford pickup, to take them to the appointment. The deep blue truck had torn seat covers and a door which had to be opened from the inside. But the tires were decent, so Uncle Carl agreed to make the day-long trip.

Leola, Dawfie, and the boys waited on the porch in the chilly March morning. "Now you boys be good for Eliza. If you are, I'll bake you a chocolate cake tomorrow." Two heads nodded as they shivered in their coats.

The boys were soon left in Eliza's care and the truck turned southeast to make the trip to Lake Charles. When Leola called from Frank's store to make the appointment, she'd carefully written down the instructions to find the doctor's office. She checked her purse once again to make sure she'd brought them.

Both were silent for most of the trip. Uncle Carl concentrated on keeping the old tires on the road while Leola watched out the window, trying to remember what she wanted to tell the doctor. Dawfie sat in the seat between the two, seeming to enjoy the movement of the pickup.

They arrived in Lake Charles two hours before the appointment. Leola turned to Uncle Carl. "Let's find a place for coffee and some breakfast. I brought enough cash to cover it."

Uncle Carl never took his eyes away from the road. "Reckon I can handle a little breakfast for us, Leola."

She nodded silently, ashamed she'd offended her husband's uncle.

Soon they were in a small diner near the doctor's clinic. A waitress wearing a bright pink uniform, a white half-hat and a white bib apron came to them as soon as they were settled in a booth near the window. The name *Verna* was scrawled on white tape across a nametag pinned to her chest. "Mornin' to ya. What can I git you folks for?" Her Cajun accent was familiar to anyone who traveled in south Louisiana.

Leola smiled, wishing to hear more of the unusual speech, but instead turned her attention to the menu. After she and Carl ordered, Verna turned to Dawfie. "And what can I git you, Cher?" She waited for a response but Dawfie sat silent, rocking in her chair, fascinated by the small red checks on the tablecloth.

Leola spoke quickly, placing an order without explaining Dawfie's behavior. Verna frowned and wrote the order on her tablet. As she walked away, she said, "I reckon some kids need better manners!"

Uncle Carl raised up out of his seat, intent on speaking to the waitress, but Leola laid her hand on his arm. "It's okay. I reckon she doesn't understand Dawfie like we do." She ducked her head so Uncle Carl wouldn't see the hurt in her eyes.

The wait in the outer office seemed endless as Dawfie, acutely aware of the smells and sights of a doctor's office, became more and more agitated. When they were called back to the exam room, Dawfie's emotional state proved close to a full-blown meltdown. The promise of an ice cream after the visit persuaded her to enter the exam room. After some resistance from the unhappy four-year-old, the doctor completed his exam, saying little to Leola.

As soon as he left, a nurse came in and sat across from Dawfie at a small table. She asked the child to play some games and identify some pictures. Dawfie gave no responses other than to grab a picture card of a baby which she clutched tightly in her fist, refusing to give it back to the nurse. The grim-faced nurse held her mouth in a tight line as she made notes on a large white clipboard.

"The doctor will be back shortly," she said, and left without another word—and without the card of the baby which Dawfie stubbornly held on to.

"Reckon you won that little battle, Daughter. But I'm not sure how much good it did you." The hope Leola had been clinging to for the days preceding this visit seemed to be disintegrating as the morning wore on.

Thirty long, frustrating minutes later, the doctor hurried back into the room holding the same white clipboard. "Mrs. Cochran, I think Dawfie has brain damage, probably from birth. She's clearly retarded. I think this is the most she will ever be." He looked not at Leola, but at the notes taken by the nurse.

Lord, give me grace. It would be wrong to say what I'm thinking about this doctor right now!

"Thank you for seeing her. I appreciate the time you've given me today, but I'll not be agreeing with you. Dawfie will get better, I'll see to it." She retrieved her purse, took Dawfie by the hand and left the room without another word.

Chapter Twenty-nine

When Dawfie was five, she began to make eye contact with her mother and brothers. She even started calling her family by names, ones she made up with her limited speech ability. She called her mother Ma. Her name for Wilburn was Teen; and Vernon, who cried a lot and was called a crybaby by his older brother, became Crowbaby.

"I've decided to send Dawfie to school this fall. I think she's ready to learn now," Leola announced. "You boys will have to look out for her." She spent the rest of the month of August making three new school dresses for her daughter.

Dry September dust bellowed behind the yellow school bus as it made its way down the river road on the first day of school. Leola helped five-year-old Dawfie up the tall steps of the bus. "You boys watch out for your sister. Make sure she's on the bus when y'all head home this afternoon."

All morning, Leola thought of Dawfie, praying school might be the answer for her. But before lunch the principal arrived at Leola's house, Dawfie in hand. "I'm sorry, Mrs. Cochran, but we can't do anything for Dawfie. It's best you keep her home from now on."

Leola reached down to take Dawfie's hand from the principal's. "Thank you for bringing her home," she responded in a tear-filled voice. Broken-hearted to know Dawfie was rejected by the school, she watched the principal's car out of sight. Looking down at her daughter in her new dress and new shoes, Leola whispered, "Don't you never mind, Dawfie. Ma's going to find a way to help you."

After getting the kids into bed, Leola sat in the front room. Some words Doc had said to her a few years ago came to mind, and this time she didn't shut them out. "Ms. Leola, I wish you'd hear me out. I've tried to say this before but you never want to listen. Charity Hospital in New Orleans will take Dawfie and help her learn things. They know how to work with a child like Dawfie. Seems like that's her best choice. Maybe her only choice. May be she wouldn't have to stay long."

The thought of sending her daughter away crushed Leola, her mother's heart unable to fathom it. But if this hospital could help Dawfie, she was willing to pray on it. Under the light of the coal oil lantern, Leola prayed long into the night, seeking an answer. The lantern grew dim, low on fuel, before Leola finally rose and went to her bedroom, her decision made. Tomorrow she would call Doc and ask him to make the arrangements.

It took only a week to get word that the hospital could take Dawfie, but she had to be there within a few days or they would give up her bed.

"I'll clear my calendar for the day after tomorrow, Mrs. Cochran. It's best I take her so I can give them Dawfie's medical history. Have her ready early; I'll pick her up just after daybreak," Doc said solemnly.

Leola spent the next day washing Dawfie's clothes and packing them in the same denim suitcase she had brought to Louisiana so many years ago. Tears filled her eyes as she remembered the places the suitcase had taken her and who she had travelled with. *Oh, John Thomas, I hope I've made the right decision. What will I do without little Dawfie at my side?*

By nightfall, everything was ready. She sat Dawfie in the kitchen as supper simmered on the stove. Taking the chair next to her, Leola tried to think of how to explain what would happen in the morning. "Dawfie, do you remember when we went on a trip with Uncle Carl and you liked riding in the pickup? Well, Doc is coming tomorrow, and you'll get an even longer ride in his car." She watched Dawfie closely, willing her to understand. The five-year-old never looked up from the small doll she clutched in both her hands. Leola sighed and reached over to stroke her daughter's hair. "It's going to be okay, I promise."

Doc arrived just as the sun peeked over the pine trees. Dawfie got excited to see his vehicle, pointing to it and repeating "Gonna" over and over.

"Yes, Dawfie, you're going to ride in the truck. But I'm not going with you this time, just you and Doc." Leola didn't know if the child understood, and the familiar sorrow of not being able to fully communicate with Dawfie filled her chest.

"Come on, Dawfie. We're going for a ride in my car." Doc grabbed the suitcase off the porch and started toward the car. Leola picked Dawfie up in an effort to hold her close and walked to the passenger's side of the truck. She settled Dawfie into the seat and placed her favorite doll in her lap.

Working hard to keep tears from falling, Leola leaned in to hug her daughter. "Be good. Show them how smart you are." She closed the door gently, stepped back and waited for Dawfie's reaction.

The tires started rolling away before Dawfie realized Leola wasn't in the truck. Loud cries lifted out the open window as Doc tried to hold Dawfie in her seat and drive away. "Ma, Ma, Ma!"

Leola clutched her apron as sobs rose within her. She released them with a force, hoping to drown out Dawfie's cries, cries she would hear for many nights to come.

The days dragged by as if time had decided to stop without the little girl living on the river road. Even Dawfie's brothers played quieter and talked less, often asking their ma, "When's Dawfie coming home?" Leola's breath caught in her throat each time they asked. Not wanting to make a promise she didn't know if she could keep, she only responded, "By and by, I reckon."

After a while, Eliza expressed her concern over the family. "Leola, honey, are you sure you want to leave Dawfie there any longer? You look awful. You're hardly eatin' and those boys o' yours don't look much better. You think maybe she's done learned enough and you can go git her now?"

Leola sat in the wagon, reins in her hands, and stared at her mule. "Reckon that's up to the specialists at the hospital. Doc said they'd call when it's time to bring her home." She started for home, not wanting to hear anything else her friend might say. Letting her mule take the lead, she knew it would slow her return home. *Lord, I can't bear being at home now without Dawfie, and seeing my boys' questioning looks is breaking my heart. Please let her come home soon.*

"Ma, come quick. Doc is here." The boys came running around the side of the house. Leola dropped the dishtowel she held to rush outside, her heart suddenly in her ears. *Dawfie's coming home!* She willed herself to stop on the porch instead of running to the car.

"Oh, Doc. I'm so glad she's coming home. I'd like to go with you this time. Don't think I can wait here as bad as I want to see her."

"Wait a minute, Leola. I need to tell you what I know first." Doc made his way to the porch, huffing by the time he sat in the first available rocker. "Missus says I need to lose some weight. Says I'd get around better if I did. She might be right." He slowly fanned himself with his fedora hat.

"Please, Doc. Tell me she's coming home. It's

been six weeks. We're missing her something awful."

"Now, Leola. You agreed to let her stay until she's better. Well, she's going to be better, but they need more time. They just discovered she has blood on her brain. It's what's been causing all her struggles. They drew it off but think they need more time to make sure it doesn't come back. It's good news, Leola. You just need to be patient and let them do their job."

Blood on her brain. Drawing it off. Leola's knees began to buckle at the image of what this procedure might involve. "Whoa, there. Maybe you should sit down, Leola." Doc moved to his feet and took Leola by the elbow, gently leading her to a rocker. "Just sit a minute and I'll try to answer your questions."

"I don't understand. She's been there so long. How can they know this now?"

"Seems a brand-new doctor just came on board. Young man from up north somewhere. They said he knew right off what the problem was. It's a miracle, Leola, that's what it is for sure."

"The only miracle I want is to see my girl sitting here in her rocker." Leola took a deep breath, knowing she had snapped at the doctor. In a calmer voice, she asked, "How much longer did they say it would take?"

"Just a few months. They need to be sure the bleeding doesn't come back."

The air swooshed from Leola's lungs. "A few months? I don't think I can wait till then. I miss her powerful bad."

"You got to stay strong, Leola. I'm sure she'll be home by Christmas. Won't that be a wonderful present,

Dawfie home and fixed good as new?" Doc grabbed his fedora and returned it to his head, "Well, I've got patients to see. I'll let you know when I hear from them again."

Leola nodded, not trusting her voice. She wanted to scream at him, telling him she didn't want to wait—couldn't wait—until Christmas.

Chapter Thirty

"Hullo to house?" Uncle Carl yelled, knocking hard on the front door. Leola came around the side of the house as he turned away from the door. A plucked chicken hung from one of his hands.

"Morning, Leola. I thought you were gone. Where's the ..." He stopped when she stepped into full view, his eyes roving over her unkempt hair, her wrinkled dress, and swollen, bloodshot eyes.

"You okay, Leola? You ain't ailin', are you?"

"I'm not ailing, Uncle Carl. Just been working at cleaning the animal's stalls. The boys usually do it, but Eliza came by and took them home with her. She said..." Leola looked to the ground, unable to admit the real cause for her appearance.

A long silence followed. Carl spoke first. "I brung you and the boys a chicken for supper. I had too many hens in my henhouse." He held the plucked chicken high in the air with a forced smile.

Leola tucked her head to her chin, shoulders shaking from tears. In a much softer voice, he said, "I'll just put 'er in the kitchen. You take a seat here on the porch. We be needin' to talk."

He disappeared through the door but returned in less than a minute. He gently moved Leola to a rocker and sat in the one next to it.

Carl sat quietly for a few moments, then spoke. "Leola, I'm a'thinkin' Dawfie is the reason for these tears."

Leola let out a sob then covered her mouth with her fist. All she could do was nod.

"I thought so. Tell me, when are these here special doctors gonna let that girl come on home?"

"Doc said maybe Christmas. But I can't wait that long. I don't feel the same as I felt when I sent her there. Can't get any peace about it now." Another sob came from Leola. This time she didn't try to smother it.

"Leola, when there be no peace, God cain't be in it. Sometimes 'hit's that easy to know His will. Reckon 'hit be time now to go get Dawfie. I'll be back first thing in the mornin'." He paused then added. "I'm a'thinkin' you might want to fix up a little before then." He stepped of the porch and walked to his truck without another word.

Leola dried her face with her dirty apron. *Thank You, Lord, for sending Uncle Carl here today. I'm at my end with fear and worry.*

When Eliza brought the boys home later in the afternoon, Leola met them in the yard wearing a clean dress, neat hair and a wide smile.

"Well, you're lookin' a whole heap better. I'm sorely glad to see it."

"I am better, Eliza. Uncle Carl is coming first thing in the morning and we're going to bring Dawfie home."

"It's about time those doctors realized a daughter needs to be with her ma. I'm glad Doc came with the news."

"Doc didn't come. Uncle Carl made me see it's not God's plan for Dawfie to stay in that place any longer. I'd be obliged if you could watch the boys tomorrow. It'll be a long day of traveling."

"Just drop 'em by in the morning. I'll have some chocolate cookies baked for Dawfie when you get back. I know'd she loves them. Shorely will be good to see her." Eliza nodded goodbye as she turned her wagon around.

Two sleepy boys were left at Eliza's house before daylight. "You boys be good. I'll be coming back with your sister." Leola kissed each boy on the top of the head before turning to Eliza. "Thank you again. I don't know what I'd do without you."

"Don't you worry none about that. Reckon I'll be dropping my two off at your house, when this new baby gets ready to come!" She waved her hand toward the truck. "Y'all go on now. Bring that young'un back where she belongs."

The trip seemed to last an eternity to Leola. She passed the time thinking of her daughter's favorite foods. She'd make them all when Dawfie came home. Eventually, she dropped off to sleep, lulled by the back and forth rocking of the truck.

"Leola, best you wake up. I reckon we're here." Uncle Carl's voice finally broke through her deep sleep.

"I'm sorry. I guess I didn't sleep much last night. Too excited."

"Well, take a look over thar. Ain't it the biggest buildin' you ever see'd?"

Leola turned to see an enormous two-story gray building, with an imposing front entrance on which the words Charity Hospital were engraved into the stone. Covering close to a city block, the building supported several wings jutting out from the main building to the north and the south.

"Oh, my," Leola breathed. "We might get lost trying to find her."

"It's okay, Leola. Reckon somebody will know where one little-bitty girl is. Let's get a-goin'."

Leola smoothed her hair as if that would give her the confidence of her husband's uncle. Then she grabbed her purse and exited the truck. The building seemed even larger this close to it.

The inside was more intimidating than the outside. Even Uncle Carl paused as if not sure what to do next. Leola was the first to act when a person in a white coat passed by. "Excuse me, sir. Can you tell us how to find someone in this place? My daughter..."

"Vous go to dat dere desk. They help you beaucoup." The man hurried on in the direction he was headed.

Leola blinked, not sure she understood the thick Cajon dialect. Uncle Carl took her elbow, pressing her forward.

"Come on, Leola. Reckon those thar people behind the desk can help us."

"R-right. I'm sorry. Yes, of course. That's what we should do." But when she got to the desk, she found she couldn't talk.

Uncle Carl stepped up to a young lady who was on the phone. "We a'lookin' for a little girl named Dawfie. We be needin' your help."

The lady held the receiver to her chest, and looked at them, waiting for more.

"We need to see a patient by the name of Doris Lucille Cochran." Leola's voice held only a slight tremor. "Can you help us?"

Without a word, the woman thumbed through a long row of cards in a wooden box. "Ward C, second floor, north wing. Take the stairs to the left and follow the signs." She rattled off the words, then returned to her phone call without another look at the two people standing before her.

"Thank you," Leola replied, hiding her irritation at the woman's shortness. "Let's go, Uncle Carl. I think we can find it."

"Just follow the signs" proved more difficult than Leola thought. After several wrong turns and the help of a kind man swathing a mop over the wood floors, they arrived at a door marked WARD C – NORTH WING. "Here it is. Do you think we should just walk in, Uncle Carl?"

"Well, we done come too far not to!" Uncle Carl

pushed open the door and held it for Leola.

The scene came to Leola in pieces. First the smell of antiseptic mixed with urine assaulted her nose. Then came sounds too sad for a mother's heart, grunts, babbles and cries. She fought the urge to cover her ears, wanting to shut out the misery around her.

Sight was the last to come as Leola focused on the room. A large room with cots placed too close together, tiny shelves holding a hodge-podge of everything from rumpled clothes to honeypots. The patients were the last to come into her view. Patients—mere children—sitting, standing and lying. Some even squatting next to their cots. What struck her most was the lack of happiness in the room. Indeed, the place seemed to exude fear on the edge of hysteria.

As Leola took in the scene, the chambers of her heart shredded bit by bit until it lay at her feet like the torn pieces of an unwelcome letter. She became unhinged, a mother bear looking for a lost cub.

"Dawfie, it's Ma. Where are you, child?" she screamed. She ran from cot to cot, getting more frantic each time the child was not her daughter. Suddenly, a sound akin to a mountain lion exploded from her mouth. "Dawfie!"

Then Leola saw her daughter standing next to a wall, rocking her torso back and forth, drool oozing down from her mouth, dripping off her chin. Leola stopped, unable to comprehend the child before her. Dawfie's hair had fallen out in great patches and she had lost weight. But worst of all were her eyes. They held nothing but a blank stare.

Two nurses, pulled to the scene by the noise, tried to approach Leola. "Ma'am, you shouldn't be here. We have a visiting room for parents. If you'll just come with..." One nurse stepped forward and took Leola's arm.

"Don't touch me! What have you people done to my daughter? I'm taking her away from this place."

"But you can't just come in here and take a patient. The doctor has to..."

Leola turned to the nurse, speaking in a low determined voice, teeth clenched together, hands pulled into tight fist. "I mean to take her now. The only way this won't happen is if you call the police. Do it if you want, but if you do, my uncle over there will be getting a *Times-Picayune News* reporter to take a picture of them dragging me out of here because that's the only way I'm leaving without my daughter."

The nurses took a step back, one turning to the other in a whisper, "I'll try to find the doctor."

The other faced Leola again, her face full of compassion. "Mrs. Cochran, we understand you miss your daughter. Maybe the doctor will let you check her out for the night. I'm sure we can find some way to fix this."

"This will get fixed when I get my daughter back home. Now, excuse me, I need to get her ready."

Quietly, she walked slowly toward her daughter. "Dawfie, it's Ma. Come to take you home, sweetheart. Uncle Carl is here. You get to ride in his truck, just what you like to do." Leola's voice broke as she continued, "Only this time, baby, I'll be riding with you."

Dawfie didn't move, just continued to rock, never looking at her mother.

Tears filled Leola's voice as she tried again. "Teen and Crowbaby miss you, Dawfie, and so do I. So badly my body has felt like it was falling apart. Let me take you home, sweetheart. It's almost time to put up the Christmas tree. I know you always like seeing the pretty tree." Sobs exploded from her chest as she watched Dawfie for any sign of agreement. "I promise I'll never send you away again."

Slowly, very slowly, Dawfie took a small step toward her. "Doll home, Ma?"

Smiling through her tears, Leola whispered, "Yes, Dawfie. Your doll can come home too."

Chapter Thirty-one

Leola put her sewing in her lap and peeked out the front window. Already, the daylight faded as night approached. She sighed as she rose from her place near the fire to examine the feed store calendar tacked on the wall nearest the kitchen. "December 7, 1941," she whispered so her boys wouldn't hear. "It's hard to believe John Thomas has been gone for nearly six years." *My very bones still miss him.*

Straightening her shoulders, she pivoted to the boys playing checkers on the floor near the fireplace. "Time to get ready for evening church." Two groans followed.

"Ma, how come we got to go to church again? Ain't Sunday morning e'nuff?" her youngest son asked.

She stared at the child who always challenged her, yet who had an ever-ready smile which warmed her heart. "It's not too much to give God our attention twice on a Sunday."

"Reckon we could give Him our attention right here in the front room?" Vernon countered.

"For that, young man, you can hitch the wagon. Now, get going. Service starts at four o'clock." She smiled as her youngest son went out the back, letting the door slam slightly harder than necessary.

Leola was thankful the church had moved the time of the night services three hours earlier after Thanksgiving, which allowed its members to travel to and from church in the daylight. She shook the reins, hoping to get there early enough for a short visit with Eliza.

When the church came into view, Leola was surprised by the number of vehicles and wagons already there. "Hurry up, kids. I must have forgotten to wind the clock. I think we're late."

Vernon perked up in his place next to Leola. "Reckon we just oughta go on back home, Ma?"

Leola ignored his comment and spoke a quick command. "Get Dawfie down and let's get inside. I don't hear any singing, must already be preaching."

Stepping into the church, Leola blinked at the unexpected scene. Instead of sitting in the pews, everyone was huddled in a tight group around the pulpit. No one spoke a word. The only noise came from voice in a static-filled radio sitting on the communion table.

Relieved to see Eliza rushing toward her, Leola grabbed her arm. "Eliza, what on earth is—"

"It's them Japs. They done attacked our ships in Hi-wa-ee. Place called Pearl Harbor. We been here awhile now. Hit the news about 2:30 and ever'body just seemed to collect here, even some of the Baptists. Preacher brought his radio. Been listening to it for pert near an hour now."

Eliza's eyes filled as she continued. "Hit's real bad, Leola. The news is saying thousands of our boys been kilt. Reckon it means war." Tears coursed down both cheeks, fear evident in her eyes. "Oh, Leola, my boys! They's seventeen next month. I s'pose they'll be a-goin'."

Stunned into silence, Leola worked to understand all she heard. Taking a breath, she squeezed her friend's arm and tried to sound calm even though her heart was beating fiercely. "Eliza, try not to borrow trouble. Let's see what the news has to say. Surely it can't be so bad."

For the next hour, the members hung to every word coming from the radio. None of it was encouraging and Leola found it exhausting. Then, there was an announcement telling them President's Roosevelt's wife, Eleanor, would continue as planned with her weekly *Over Our Coffee Cups* radio program. The crowd didn't seem ready to leave yet, though a few ladies had moved to the pews, silently crying into their hankies while the men wandered back and forth from outside to smoke or chew.

Leola peered at the remaining daylight, hoping there was enough time to listen to the First Lady's program. She'd been an admirer of Mrs. Roosevelt, following her duties as First Lady in the newspapers. *I'd surely like to hear what a woman thinks of this attack.*

Everyone agreed they would listen to the

program, then leave for home before it was too dark. Leola nodded in agreement with the rest, eager to her what Mrs. Roosevelt had to say. Instinct told her they might find comfort from this amazing lady.

She wasn't disappointed. As the first public speaker to address the nation following the attack on American soil, Mrs. Roosevelt's steady and encouraging voice brought a measure of peace to a rattled nation. Leola and the other women in the room were especially impressed by her call for women to do their part to aid the efforts of what surely would be a war against Japan.

When the program ended, the pastor led the group in prayer, asking for God's grace on the families who had lost sons and daughters at Pearl Harbor and for His mercy in the days ahead. A silent group headed out, with little to say.

What can we say? Leola thought as she ushered her crew to their wagon. *Our lives will change again, just like they did when the Depression hit. Lord, give us strength.*

The next day, President Roosevelt asked Congress for a Declaration of War against the Empire of Japan.

"Hullo, the house."

Leola smiled as she walked to the front door, knowing Uncle Carl's familiar greeting. It was her first smile since the alarming church gathering the evening before. Still hoping the first news wasn't as bad as it seemed, she welcomed a chance to visit with him. She opened the door, letting Uncle Carl and a gust of cold air enter. Seeing the look on his face evaporated her hopes like rainwater disappearing on a hot day.

"I brung you my old Farm Radio, Leola. I brought a new one from Frank's store this mornin'. He only had one for sale, so I snatched it right up. Figure folks may make a run on them now, what with the attack and Lord knows what else. This one here's battery operated and I just put some new ones in. Should last you a while, iff'n you don't play it too much. I'm thinkin' you be needin' to keep up with news these days." It was a mouthful from a man not known to be long on words. He was silent then, as if not sure what to do next.

Leola hurried to move a picture frame from the small corner table. "Reckon this will do to set it on?"

Uncle Carl paused, looking at the table and back to the radio, then offered a small suggestion of a smile. "Reckon so. Hits always best to set these things out of the way of rambunctious kids. Easy to knock over." Once the radio was sitting on the table, he hurried to show Leola how to find stations. "This here's the station you'll get best. The rest are likely to have lotta static."

"Uncle Carl, I surely do thank you. It'll be good to not have to wait until I can get a newspaper to know the news." Leola stood, hands folded in front of her, looking at the radio. It would not only bring her news; it might alleviate some of the loneliness sure to come in the long days ahead. She turned back to Uncle Carl with a wide smile. "Come spring when the dewberries are ready, I'm going to make you a big cobbler. I know how much you like them."

Uncle Carl grinned. "Well, I'll sorely look forward

to that. Right now, I need to get on back home. President Roosevelt will be talkin' on the radio soon. Reckon what's he got to say might be important. Don't want to miss it."

Leola watched the man walk to his wagon. "Whatever made me afraid of him when John Thomas and I first married? He's just a big softy."

Chapter Thirty-two

Life changed quickly after Pearl Harbor. Cousins and young men from the community either joined up or were drafted into the military. Leola watched as Eliza and Silas said a teary good-bye to the twins. Her own tears added to those of the parents as she remembered the rowdy toddlers who scrambled around in the back of a wagon the first time she met them. Privately, she thanked God her two sons were only twelve and fourteen, too young yet to be seen off to war.

Before long, meat, coffee, sugar, chocolate and eggs were rationed. Leola learned ways to stretch her rations by substituting ingredients when cooking. The radio continued to be a source of both war information and entertainment for her family. The boys loved The Lone Ranger and Major League Baseball. One day while turning the knob on the radio, Leola stumbled onto The Grand Ole' Opry and rarely missed it thereafter.

She often listened to a cooking program where

she got recipes of for baking. War Cake became a favorite. Made without eggs or sugar, the dense cake used molasses, spices and boiled raisins. Dawfie loved it, often taking bags of raisins off the pantry shelf and laying them on the table—her way of communicating her desire for Leola to make one.

As with the Depression, it seemed like the war would never end. News came almost daily now of someone from the community being killed or injured. Eliza's boys were serving on a ship and, although their parents didn't know where, letters from the twins confirmed they'd been allowed to stay in the same unit.

"At least they's together, Leola. Don't reckon I could stand it if they weren't. They ain't been separated a day in their lives." Leola noted her friend had aged since the start of the war, worry evident in the new lines in her face and a slowness of the smile which everyone had come to love.

One day, four years after the attack on Pearl Harbor, Vernon didn't get off the bus with his brother. Leola's heart constricted, trying to hold in the fear rising in her body. In a sudden flash of memory, she recalled sixteen-year-old Vernon's statement the night before when they were listening to the war news: "Reckon I'll be over there fighting soon." She'd just heard a few days ago how many young boys were lying about their age to join the military. *Surely, he hasn't tried to join up.*

"Where's Vernon?" she asked Wilburn, desperately trying to keep her voice normal.

"He got off at Frank's store. Said he'd walk the rest of the way home."

Relief coursed through her with the knowledge he was only a half a mile away and not in Merryville at the recruiting office. She stepped onto the porch, waiting to see her youngest son walking up the road. She heard his whistle before he came into view.

"Hey, Ma," he yelled when he got close to their yard. "I stopped off at Frank's store to get us some apple butter. I already opened it to get a taste; reckon it'll be good on some of your biscuits." His grin spread from ear to ear. "I put it on our tab."

"Vernon Earl, what are you thinking? You know I don't have any sewing funds coming in. There's no money for apple butter." Leola voice trembled with anger more from the fear of her son joining the war than the purchase he made without permission. Countless times she'd wished John Thomas was here to help counsel their impulsive middle child. Suddenly, it came to her how to best handle the situation.

"Sit here in the rocker. I'll be right back." In a short moment, she came back onto the porch and handed him a spoon. "Don't stop eating until the spoon hits the empty bottom of the jar. When you finish, we have some talking to do."

Red dirt from the dry September day blew up behind the vehicle careening down the river road. Leola straightened from where she'd bent to gather squash and turnips, the last her garden would produce this year, and watched as the truck squeaked to a stop perilously close to her front gate. The door flew open as Eliza tumbled out so quickly her stout body stumbled when she hit the ground.

"Leola, the war's over! My boys are comin' home!"

"Praise God," Leola said as she pulled Eliza into a tight embrace, tears wetting the shoulders of each other's dress.

Stepping back, Leola's gaze went to the truck. The driver's door hung open, the motor still running. "I thought you were afraid to drive Silas's truck. When did you learn how?"

"I don't reckon I did." She smiled as she wiped tears with her apron. "Hit's my first time drivin'. Just couldn't take the time to hitch up my wagon to git here to tell you the good news. Reckon pure happiness just ended my fear of drivin' that rickety ol' thing."

Later in the evening, Leola prayed over the evening meal. "Thank you, Lord, that the war is over. Thank You for bringing our troops back home. Help us to always remember those who aren't returning and the bravery they've shown to keep us safe from the enemy. Thank You for the food we are about to eat and for all Your provisions, Lord, during these past four years. Amen." She sat with her hands in her lap and her head down, not yet able to eat what was before her. *And, Lord, thank You this war ended before my sons were old enough to fight. I pray our country will never be at war again.*

Chapter Thirty-three

During the post-war years, women again found their way to the river road with sewing for Leola. The boys, now sixteen and eighteen, were old enough to do men's chores, so she found herself with time to sew. Like his father, Vernon loved to hunt and fish. He often brought home a welcomed food supply. Even Dawfie helped out some. She'd learned to serve a cup of coffee, do the dishes, and make the beds.

One Saturday, Leola walked to the front porch, hat on her head and a handbag over one arm. The boys were sitting on the porch, each head stuck in a book, while Dawfie sat cross-legged on the ground watching her cat. "Boys, I'm going to the store. I need some sewing thread. Y'all watch your sister. I'll be back shortly."

"Yes'm," they mumbled without lifting their heads from their books.

Leola intended to go to the store and right back, a twenty-minute walk both ways. Ten to fifteen minutes in the store would put her home in an hour, maybe less. However, two ladies from church were at the mercantile and wanted to talk about dinner on the grounds coming up the last Sunday of the month. The ladies went on to chat about the abundance of fabric filling the store's shelves again and who in the community awaited the arrival of a new baby.

Leola glanced at the clock on the shelf behind the cash register and realized she had been in the store for forty-five minutes. "Goodness, I'd better get home. I told the boys I wouldn't be long." Making her good-byes, she tucked the thread into her purse, hurried out the door, and turned onto the county road which led to the river road. She walked quickly, which with her height and long legs proved significantly faster than most. She smiled as she thought of how she'd always had to slow her gait for her much shorter husband. *That's okay, John Thomas, never minded slowing up for you.*

A dark cloud suddenly blocked the sunlight when she turned on the river road, casting a gray shadow all about. Leola shivered, a chill running over her body not caused by the temperature. Her breathing quickened though she couldn't have said why. "Really, Leola, you're letting yourself get spooked for no reason." Still, she increased her speed, even more eager to be home.

The boys were on still on the porch engrossed in their books. Leola looked to the side yard where Dawfie had been playing. She wasn't there, nor anywhere else in sight.

"Boys, where's Dawfie? Is she in the house?" She raced past her sons without waiting for a response, her voice gaining volume with each step.

"Dawfie, are you in here? Where are you, sweet girl? Tell Ma where you are." Only silence met her pleas. She rushed back to the porch where the boys now stood, blinking like a couple of frogs caught in a hailstorm. The reality of Dawfie missing hit her. Fear began at her feet and moved upward and outward, saturating her body. It propelled her into action.

"Wilburn, you go up the river road. If you don't find her by the time you're at the river, turn and go to Uncle Carl's house. Get his help. We may need his truck."

"Vernon, you go through the woods to the creek and follow it to the river from there." Leola's mouth was now dry as cotton. She put her arms around her middle to keep her body from flying in every direction, then continued.

"When you spot her, don't yell. If she thinks you're mad, she may bolt. I'll stay here in case she comes…where's Coonie? Oh, Lord, has she followed that old cat off somewhere?" No longer able to stand on her legs, Leola dropped into the nearest rocker. "Get going, boys. Find your sister."

The boys bolted off the porch, each moving to their assigned direction. At the edge of the yard, Vernon stopped and turned back. "Don't worry, Ma. We'll find her. I'm sorry…" His voiced wavered as he turned and plunged into the woods, choosing the most direct route instead of following the cleared trail.

Leola watched him until he was out of sight, hearing his soft words exactly the way she warned. "Dawfie, come see Crowbaby. How about I whittle you a new baby doll?"

She sat for a long moment, her mind caught in a whirlwind spiraling downward to a place she knew she shouldn't go. Putting her elbows on her knees, she covered her face and began to pray. How long she stayed this way she didn't know. At the sound of someone running, she popped her head up, listening intently.

"Ma, I found her," Vernon said from the edge of the yard, the woods making a wall behind him. "I need help. She fell down the creek bank."

Leola was on her feet and off the porch in two strides. With Vernon in the lead, she followed close behind, ducking the branches he pushed aside as he returned the way he had come out.

Lord, please let her be all right became her mantra with every step she took. After what seemed like an eternity, they were finally at the creek, looking down at a spot where its bank fell into a steep decline.

Dawfie hung just above the water, holding on to a large, gnarly tree root sticking out the sides of the bank. Her feet dangled in the moving water, her hands wrapped around the root with a death grip. Small grunts came from her mouth, her eyes never moving from the water below her.

"Oh, Lord in heaven!" Leola pulled her eyes from Dawfie to ask Vernon, "What do we do? I can't think. How will we get to her?"

Vernon shook his head, fear evident in his eyes. "I don't know. If we spook her, she might lose her grip. If she goes in the water..."

The noise of a vehicle on the trail drew their

attention away from the creek. Uncle Carl and Wilburn were out of the truck almost before it rolled to a stop. Vernon made a hush sign with his finger over his lips and pointed down to the creek. Assessing the situation, Uncle Carl began giving orders in a quiet, authoritative voice.

"Wilburn, git the rope from the back of the truck. Vernon, yer a-gonna shimmy down the bank jest to the left of her. She's turned mostly to the right, maybe she won't see you comin' at her. Tie this rope around yer waist. We'll tie the other end to the bumper of the truck. Reckon we all need to be a-movin' slow and quiet-like so's we don't scare her none." His stern glance at each family member reinforced his commands.

He turned back to Vernon, "When you git to her, wrap yer arms around her and hold on as tight as you can. Wilburn'll drive the truck slowly back to pull you up. Jist make sure you got her tight. You also gotta protect her from hittin' against the bank. Put your body 'tween hers and anythin' that can hurt her. I'll lay on the edge of the bank so's I can help git her on over when you git to the top. Can you do this?"

Vernon nodded, "Y'sir, I got it." He tied the rope around his waist with the help of his brother, using a strong double knot they'd learned from one of their books. They searched for a good place near Dawfie's left for his descent.

Leola stood near the scene praying. *Lord, give them each the strength they need to do this. And let Dawfie not resist Vernon when he grabs her and holds her close.*

When everyone was in place, Uncle Carl nodded for Vernon to begin working his way down the bank. Leola was sure time had stopped as her son inched his way closer to Dawfie. Emotions warred in her body, wanting him to go faster, yet knowing he needed to move slowly so as not to frighten the girl.

Suddenly, she remembered the scripture she'd read in her bible that morning in the book of Psalms: "My steps have held fast to your path, my feet have not slipped." She lowered her head. *Thank You for Your Word. Help me to trust in You now.*

When she raised her head, Vernon had successfully grabbed Dawfie and motioned for help to come up. She marveled at the way Dawfie allowed her brother to hold her close without trying to wrangle away from him as she usually did when anyone tried to embrace her. *Little girl, you seem to know the danger, don't you?*

Uncle Carl relayed the message to Wilburn with his hands, still wanting to be as quiet as possible. The old truck went into reverse and began slowly rolling back without even a groan. Leola's eyes filled with tears as she watched her daughter and son inch their way up the bank. When they neared the top, Uncle Carl reached down to clasp Vernon's arms and heave the pair to the flat ground.

The tears Leola held at bay now flowed freely as she sat on the ground and gathered Dawfie close in her arms. She patted Vernon on the back as he sat near them panting for air after his trip up the creek bank. "Thank you, Son, you did good. You too, Wilburn." All anger at her sons' neglect dissipated in a flood of relief.

Through her tears, Leola glanced over to Uncle Carl. "Don't you ever sell that old blue truck. It's surely a vehicle of God's own doing."

Chapter Thirty-four

Leola laid her blue dress on the bed, the same dress she'd worn two years before when Wilburn graduated, trying to decide if it needed an ironing before putting it on for Vernon's graduation ceremony. She fiddled with the neck ruffle, trying to make it lay straight as her mind traveled back to the boys' growing up years.

Raising them alone hadn't been easy, but John Thomas would be proud of the young men they were now—and doubly proud they both finished high school. Wilburn even choose to go to business school in Lake Charles, where he'd married and would soon become a father. Leola smiled for what must be the thousandth time at the thought of a grandbaby. *Wish you could be here to meet your first grandchild, John Thomas.*

Back in the kitchen she checked her cake to see if it was cooled. She wanted to make sure the frosting set so it would travel well to the school gymnasium.

Cake finished, she called Dawfie in from the porch to get dressed and then she readied herself. Before long, mother and daughter sat on the porch watching the river road for their ride, the old blue truck.

Leola's eyes wandered from the road to the wall of trees lining the opposite side. The same virgin pines she saw on her first trip down the river road as a new bride towered high, unchanged in all these years. So much had happened, and how different things were from what she thought her life would bring. Scenes from long ago churned in her mind.

The wind gently blew through the trees' tall tops and sparrows chirped their songs beneath the trees looking for the seeds among the pinecones, reminding her of the song "His Eye is On the Sparrow."

Lord, You've cared for me all these years, just as You care for those little sparrows over there. With both my boys soon to be moved away, help me know You'll care for me and Dawfie in the future.

The chugging of Uncle Carl's truck brought her out of her reverie. *Time to get on with whatever life brings next.*

The months after Vernon left home for a job in Ruston were lonely for Leola and Dawfie. Repeatedly Dawfie asked if Crowbaby was coming home, to which Leola had no clear answer.

Before leaving home, Vernon convinced his mother to have electricity installed. After a week of listening to his reasons, she finally relented and told him to contact the electrical company for installation. Fortunately, an electrical line had already been installed at the start of the river road, close enough to make it logical to run a line to her house. Minimum wiring done inside allowed for an overhead light in each room.

Apparently, Vernon thought he was on a roll because on his next visit, he began telling her the advantages of having a phone installed. She resisted until his final plea before leaving: "If you got a phone, us boys can call anytime, and I'll bet Wilburn will call when the grandbaby is born."

This caught her attention. "All right, Son. I'll go to Frank's store and call to have one installed. But don't you start harping about a car. I've done fine all these years without one and plan to continue to do so."

With a phone in the house, Leola found an attachment to friends and family she had never known—and even to others in the community through the party line, which brought a temptation to listen in on others' calls. On the day Wilburn called to say he had a new baby girl who looked like John Thomas, her heart overflowed with blessings.

By 1951, Leola and Dawfie had adjusted to living alone. By now Wilburn had two children, who were a joy when they came up from Lake Charles for a visit. Vernon still worked in Ruston and now made frequent visits to see a young lady in a small town back in Texas.

One morning, just before noon, Vernon's car drove into the yard. Leola left the sink where she was washing the lunch dishes, surprised to see him home on a weekday. She walked onto the porch drying her hands on her apron as he stepped out of his car. "Hello, Son. What are you doing here on a Tuesday?"

"Hello, Ma. Let's get some coffee and sit in the kitchen. It's too cold out in the yard."

Soon they were by the fire. "Best say what's on your mind, Vernon. Did you get fired from your job?"

Vernon took a long swallow of his coffee before looking at his mother. "I didn't get fired, Ma. I got drafted. Reckon I'll be shipped to Korea before long."

Leola blinked. Bits and pieces of recent news came slowly into focus. *North and South Korea, 38th parallel, President Truman announcing a major military operation, stem the spread of communism, end to hostilities...* Her head said to bring her random thoughts together so she could respond to her son, but her heart held everything at bay as though it would annul her son's announcement. After a moment, she realized Vernon was still talking.

"... I'll head off to Fort Chaffee, Arkansas for basic training in a couple of weeks. I need you to know I plan to marry that sweet little Texas girl before I go." Vernon sat silently then, waiting for his mother to catch up with all the news.

Leola realized her son needed understanding from his mother. Pushing down the fear of her son leaving for war, she spoke with a tear-filled voice. "I reckon you're man enough to handle marriage and a war, Son. Just know I'll be praying for you every day till you're back home."

Chapter Thirty-five

Vernon left on a cool day in May. "Good-bye, Ma. Reckon I'll be home as soon as I get things settled over there in Korea." Leola's mouth pulled into a small smile. Even now her middle son could find a way to make her smile. "You just keep your head down and come home to us and that wife of yours. God be with you, Son." She hugged him tightly, then stood by his car until he was behind the wheel. Returning to the porch, she and Dawfie watched the car move out of sight.

"Crowbaby home, Ma?" asked Dawfie.

Leola hesitated, not trusting her voice in the moment. She took several deep swallows, then whispered, "By and by, I reckon. By and by."

Once again, Leola sat before the radio each evening to hear war news. Most of it was confusing and did little to ease her mother's heart. She walked to the store to check her mail every day the weather permitted, hoping to see the red and white striped airmail envelop indicating a letter from Vernon.

At first the letters were frequent, full of descriptions of Korea and life in a foxhole. Leola always read the letter before leaving the store, then read it again to Dawfie in the evening, which prompted Dawfie's much-repeated question, "Crowbaby home, Ma?"

"By and by, I reckon, Dawfie," became her standard response.

After several months, Vernon's letters arrived less frequently and were more about missing them than about the war. One morning, Leola found Dawfie standing on the front porch holding on to one of the posts. She stayed there for a long time—long enough to concern Leola, who finally opened the door to call her inside. "Dawfie, why don't you come in now? How about a cookie and glass of milk?"

Dawfie didn't move, never taking her eyes off the road. "Crowbaby home, Ma?"

Leola's heart squeezed. How could she help Dawfie understand? A thought she had been dallying with for some time surfaced. For months she'd been saving money to buy a small organ for Dawfie. She'd found it in the Sears Roebuck catalog, dog-eared the page and returned to it often to consider the purchase. Even though Dawfie seemed drawn to the piano at the community center, Leola wasn't sure her daughter would pay any attention to an organ. Still, something urged her to make the purchase. The next day she went to the store to purchase a money order, filled out the order form and put both of them in the mail.

The organ arrived a month later and sat unnoticed by Dawfie, even though Leola occasionally wandered over to strike a key. She watched Dawfie carefully, disappointed when her daughter continued to ignore the instrument. Two weeks went by before Dawfie walked to the corner and stopped in front of the organ, hitting one note after another with her forefinger, her head cocked to the side.

Leola watched without saying a word. She knew Dawfie could be as stubborn as a mule if pushed to do something. *Best to let her make this decision*.

Later in the day, Dawfie took an old hymnal from the shelf in the front room and sat in the chair in front of the organ. Placing the book on the holder, she flipped through the pages, finally choosing a page. Then, to Leola's amazement, she played *The Old Rugged Cross* flawlessly. When finished, she flipped through the hymnal again, then proceeded to play more hymns, hymns she'd heard in church all her life, each song without an error.

With tears silently flowing, Leola whispered, "Sweet girl, how talented you are!"

Dawfie stopped after playing five hymns through and moved across the room to her chair to resume rocking her doll. Curious about the hymnal, Leola walked to the organ. The songbook sat wrong side up and opened to a different hymn than the last one Dawfie had played.

She stood awed not only at her daughter's ability to play the organ but also at her attempt to carry out normal actions such as finding songs in a hymnal she couldn't read. Leola thanked God for this amazing child who brought such joy to her and to so many others.

The winter after Vernon left for Korea, Eliza passed away. Leola's friend had hidden the growth in her abdomen from everyone until she could no longer bear the pain. By the time Eliza told Curtis, her body was racked with the cancer. As Leola watched her friend struggle, the same helplessness she'd experienced with John Thomas's death flooded through her.

She helped out as much as she could nursing Eliza when Curtis needed a break. She begged the Lord to let her friend live. *Lord, I can't take another loss. This lady got me through so many tough times. I love her, please don't let her die.* In the end, Leola prayed for Eliza to pass, wanting her sweet friend out of pain.

For a month after Eliza's passing, Leola could barely function. She went through her days in a daze, consumed with her grief over losing her friend and the thought that the next funeral might be her son's.

Uncle Carl came by one afternoon and over a cup of coffee, he spoke sternly with Leola. "Seems to me like you been carryin' around one big lump of pity, Leola. Don't reckon Eliza or your son would want that. Your walk with God has gotten me and plenty others through many o' tough days. For myself, I'd kinda like to see that faith again. Always helped me, somehow."

He was quiet then, finishing the last of his coffee. He sat his cup on the table and stood up. "Reckon I done said what I come to say." With that he returned his hat to his head and moved out the door.

Uncle Carl's reprimand filled Leola with embarrassment. "Help me, Father," the only prayer she could muster. Slowly, the Holy Spirit soothed her grief and bolstered her soul. She rose and carried her cold coffee to the kitchen, dumping it down the drain. "Dawfie, let's walk to the store and see if there's a letter from Vernon."

In June, news came saying Vernon would be shipped home. Leola prayed a prayer of rejoicing and praise, then wondered how to help Dawfie understand it could still be weeks before her brother would actually be home.

A month later, Leola and Dawfie sat on the porch watching for Vernon's car to come down the river road. When they finally heard the old car's motor, Dawfie stood and held on to the porch post. "Crowbaby" was all she said.

Leola ran to the front gate. Vernon jumped out of the car as soon as it stopped, grabbing his mother in a big bear hug.

"Glory be, Son, you're home," Leola was unable to say more, volumes of tears wetting the private's uniform.

Finally, Vernon released his mother and they turned to where Dawfie had been standing on the porch. She wasn't there, but notes of the gospel song *Sweet By and By* drifted out the front door and down the river road.

Part III
1952-1992

Come to me, all you who are weary and burdened
and I will give you rest.
Matthew 11:28

Chapter Thirty-six

My twin and I were born on February 19, 1952, when most families were listening to *Your Cheatin' Heart* on the radio or gathered around the television to laugh at the *I Love Lucy* show. Our family at the time consisted of our mother, her parents and three of Mom's siblings. My grandparents scratched out a living as renters and caretakers of a small farm in East Texas.

Dad came home from Korea when we were eight months old, having left a new bride and returned to a wife and two children. Times were tough for the married couple. Mom, barely eighteen years old, struggled to adjust to two babies and a husband who was plagued with what at the time was called shell shock, now known as Post Traumatic Stress Syndrome.

Jobs were scarce and the need to move out of our grandparents' already-crowded house added to the stress of the couple reuniting after over a year of separation. What ensued was a fourteen-year journey of our father going from job to job, moving his family up and down the Texas coast, not settling anywhere long enough to call it home.

As young girls, we visited Granny Leola on most holidays and for an occasional funeral of a family member. I loved going to the river road, where I was enchanted by the woods, the wall of tall pine trees across the road from the house, and the steady thumping of an oil well close enough to hear but too far away to see. I imagined a kind, gentle giant lumbering his way to the river road, crushing trees as he walked.

The inside of Granny Leola's house captivated my little girl's fancy, too. The jelly jar filled with old buttons, some still holding bits of the thread which had attached them to a piece of clothing, was a testament to my granny's penchant for saving things and "making do." I love that she modeled recycling long before it became trendy. The tiny wall shelf hanging in the front room never left its place and always held only the small resin horses given to Dawfie as gifts. Best of all was the snuff jar and spitting cup tucked underneath her chair next to the wall in the front room. I once asked her why she kept them there. "In case the preacher comes visiting," she explained.

The concept of keeping things in the same place in the same house year after year warmed the soul of a little girl who'd seen too many things lost or thrown out in too many moves.

I heard the phone conversation through the

screen door. Not many calls came to our house, so when one did, I shamelessly eavesdropped. Hearing my father respond to the caller with "Yes'm" and "No'm" confirmed Granny Leola as the person on the other end of the line.

When I heard the words "revival week" and "twins," it only took a moment to come to the realization that Granny Leola wanted my twin and me to come stay with her during revival week. I wasn't sure what *revival* might mean, but a week at my granny's sounded wonderful.

Before the phone conversation ended, Dad had agreed to bring us to Granny Leola's for the week. What followed was a night of yelling between my parents, our mother not happy with Dad for saying yes.

It hadn't occurred to him that we didn't own "church clothes." Mama knew we'd need dresses and shoes, neither of which we ever had in the summer months. Eventually, Dad won, and Mom spent a frantic week sewing each of us a couple of dresses, then scraping together the money for new shoes.

We arrived at Granny's on a scathing hot Saturday afternoon. Daddy stayed the night, then left early the next morning, having abandoned the idea of churchgoing as soon as he left home after graduation from high school. "Got to get on home to Veta and the other two girls, Ma." Nobody was fooled, least of all Granny Leola.

"Come on, girls, let's get inside. Maybe it'll be cooler when we get settled on a pew." Granny hustled us out of her neighbor's vehicle and into the church.

I stepped just inside the door, taking the scene in with one swoop. The church had wooden floors, shiplap walls and long, tall windows which lined the side walls. The pews were made of narrow wooden slats which I soon discovered left stripe marks on the back of my legs.

The ladies wore print dresses with an abundance of lace and ruffles and hats secured to their hair. The men wore rumpled suits with shirts buttoned to the neck and thin ties. Each carried a hat in their hands, having taken it off when they entered the building. Why the women left their hats on and the men removed theirs remained a mystery to me.

The room was hot even though the windows were open. I soon realized paper fans lay sporadically on the pews. The ladies used them with amazing skill, able to create a quick subtle snapping sound all around the church. I grabbed one as we headed down the aisle behind Granny Leola. "Look, Lynn. It has a picture of Jesus's head." Lynn glanced at the picture and turned away, not impressed.

Soon the building was filled to the brim, bringing the temperature up significantly. The ladies fanned harder and the men wiped their brows with large white handkerchiefs. Parents flanked their youngsters on each side, giving low-spoken admonitions to behave. I wondered what they could possibly do wrong, wedged as they were between two large adults. Lynn and I smothered a giggle when one mother pinched the side of the leg of her young squirmy son, causing him to yelp.

My twin and I had never attended a church

service, so we copied whatever we saw our grandmother doing. When she stood for singing, so did we. When she bowed her head for prayer, we bowed ours, although admittedly I peeked around, curious as to whether everyone actually bowed their heads. Watching the song leader proved entertaining as he waved one arm in the air repeating the same smooth movement over and over with the songbook in his other hand.

Following the singing, the preacher rose and moved to the pulpit. He began by quietly reading from the bible. When he laid the bible aside, his voice rose suddenly and dramatically to full volume. I grabbed my sister's hand, unsure why the man was angry. Glancing around, no one else seemed to find his behavior alarming, but I still held Lynn's hand, my ever-present protector.

Rationalizing his bizarre behavior, I decided he must be yelling so the older crowd could hear, although I couldn't determine why he waved his arms wildly about. I soon picked out a pattern in his speech which intrigued me. With amazing consistency, every word at the end of each sentence moved up a pitch. What resulted was a singsong style of speech I've rarely heard since.

Curiosity grew to such a level I finally leaned over to Granny Leola and whispered, "Granny, why is he using such a loud funny voice?"

She put her mouth close to my ear. "So he can get the attention of all the sinners here."

I held my twin's hand even tighter, not daring to look around at the sinners.

The service lasted forever, the hard pew growing more and more uncomfortable. Finally it was over, and I was antsy to get back to Granny Leola's and take off my new shoes.

After a short rest back at Granny Leola's house where my toes got a blessed reprieve, we went back for night service. How different from the morning service! The opened, screen-bare windows allowed bugs to be drawn in by the overhead lights. The ladies now used the Jesus head fans to swat the pesky critters away. I decided it was far too dangerous to sing, sure a bug would end up down my throat.

Worst of all was the trip to the outhouse behind the church. After getting Granny's permission, I grabbed Lynn's hand.

"Come with me," I begged.

"No way. It's dark out there." Lynn returned to singing.

"You have to come. I have to go...now!" I squirmed on the pew and squeezed her hand even harder.

Finally, she came with me and we quietly moved down to aisle and exited the church. The outhouse was down a narrow path lined with bushes and low overhead branches. Any stumble to the right or left meant something would brush your legs or face. In the dark, there was no way to know if it might be an animal.

At the outhouse, I went in while Lynn stood outside. Within seconds she began to whisper repeatedly, "Hurry, I'm scared!" I didn't even try to explain about the scary, deep, black hole on which I perched.

On the return trip, a hoot owl scooted both of

us inside the church door faster than a pair of rabbits. Needless to say, the week became our first experience of practicing bladder control.

When it was time to go to bed, Granny Leola tucked us in, then proceeded with what became a nightly ritual. "Nighty-night. Don't let the bedbugs bite." Then she said the most reassuring thing I'd heard all day: "Your old granny loves you."

On Tuesday afternoon, the Bookmobile came to Granny Leola's. She ushered us out to the waiting vehicle while explaining, "Now, y'all each pick out two books. This way, you'll have four books to read while you're here this week. I'm allowed five on my card so I can still get one for me."

I was fascinated with the idea of books literally coming to Granny Leola's door. Having never been in any library except at school, the fact that this library had wheels and could roll up anywhere impressed me greatly.

After we made our selections, we lay on an old quilt on the floor with a fan blowing over us and enjoyed our books. It filled the time between the morning service and the night service.

One afternoon Granny Leola asked us to deliver some eggs to our Aunt Mertie and Uncle Tom who lived not far away. A visit to their house usually ensured leaving with a handful of orange slice candies, so we were eager to carry out her request.

I loved to go there for the candy but also for the concrete walkway up to their front door, an oddity for the area. I'd seen many concrete walks but never one like my aunt and uncle's. All along both sides of the walk, small marbles had been carefully placed in the cement when it was still wet, turning an ordinary path into something magical, full of color, and a great place to make-believe everything from fairy princesses to majestic castles.

Like any fairy tale, this one had a villain—or two. Uncle Tom owned a goose and a gander that had free range of their yard. Most of the time we could handle the birds, but if they had a nest, they became very aggressive.

Lynn and I were on the lookout for the scary pair before we ever reached the front gate. "I don't see them. Let's go on in," Lynn said, showing a bravery I didn't feel.

"Wait, what if one of them comes from around the side of the house? Where do we run?"

"Quit being such a baby. Just shoo it off. And don't drop the eggs. We'll never get any candy if all we deliver are broken shells."

My head said my twin was correct, but my heart beat out a solid "no" right down to my bare feet.

We stepped inside the gate and made three steps on the sidewalk when I began to relax and enjoy looking at the marbles. Then we heard the ominous honk followed by hissing. Sure enough, the gander came running around the corner of the house at full speed.

I grabbed the back of Lynn's shirt, twisting her around so she was between me and the villain.

"Let go of me and don't just stand there—run!"

We hit the porch in three long strides, the gander right on my heals. Uncle Tom heard the ruckus and had the door open for us.

"Come on in, twins. I reckon that old gander would've only nibbled on you a bit. Mertie a'ready fed him this morning, so he's just wantin' a little snack," he cackled, amused by two scared girls.

No amount of orange slices made it worth being the gander's afternoon snack. I immediately began worrying about the trip back down the magical sidewalk. Gripping the orange slices tight in my hand, we made it down the walkway and out the gate without a goose attack. Just in case, I was ready to offer my coveted candy to the scary critters if they showed up.

Back at Granny's, we lay on the floor in the front room enjoying our books and our orange slices when a loud knock caused us to jerk to our knees.

"Leola, you home? I brung some fabric. Need me a new dress for my family reunion in a few weeks." A large black lady stood just outside the screen door, peering into the front room.

We scrambled to our feet just as our granny walked through from the kitchen.

"Come on in, Polly Mae. I just put some fresh coffee on the stove. I'll get us a cup and we can visit."

"I'd surely welcome that, Leola. Seems like the walk here gets longer the older I get." She laughed a belly laugh, her extra-large girth shaking like Jell-O.

I pressed my lips together to hold in a laugh at the sight of the women squeezing herself into one of the small chairs at the dining table. Lynn wasn't so discreet, as a loud guffaw escaped her lips.

Granny Leola turned, placing one hand on her

hip. "You girls go on back to your books. Polly Mae and I have some visiting to catch up on, then we need to talk about this new dress."

An hour later, Polly Mae left her fabric with a picture of a dress torn from the Sears Roebuck catalog on the table. At the door, she fished three quarters from her purse and handed them to Granny Leola. "You still charging seventy-five cents? Don't seem like enough for that fancy dress we done picked out, with them buttons down the front and all those ruffles."

"I reckon seventy-five cents will cover it, Polly Mae. Come back at the end of next week. I should have everything done except the hemming. I'll need you here to measure the length. We can have a good visit while you wait for the dress to be finished."

"I'll see you a week from this Friday then." Polly Mae nodded her goodbyes and headed out toward the river road for her long walk home.

Years later, I recalled the evening my grandmother visited with Polly Mae when, as a freshman in high school, the nation began mandatory school integration. Our mother sat us down the night before school started. "Now girls, tomorrow might not be easy, what with this integration and all. But I expect my girls to be kind to everyone, regardless of who they are. Don't let me hear any stories of you girls treating anyone different because of the color of their skin."

A few weeks later, our home economics teacher arrived at our door on a required teacher's visit. Mrs. Griggs may have been the tidiest woman I've ever known. She always wore a dress so heavily starched and impeccably ironed she could have been in a clothing advertisement. Impressed by the way she listened to her students with respect and interest, always responding with kind, soft word, I often engaged in a conversation with her before or after class. Only her eyes revealed her discomfort in being in a new setting. Having come from the closed black high school, she'd spent the beginning of school in unease at her change in assignment.

When our mother invited Mrs. Griggs inside and offered her a cup of coffee, tears welled up in my teacher's eyes as she mumbled a thank you and moved to a place on our couch. Watching her struggle not to cry, I knew instantly she'd probably not received such a welcome from many of the white parents.

The way my granny accepted Polly Mae as not just a customer but also as a friend and the way my mother so graciously invited Mrs. Griggs into our home at a time when it wasn't consider the thing to do among white people modeled acceptance of the differences among people in a very real way.

Chapter Thirty-seven

My sister and I had soon read all four books and were quite bored. Granny Leola announced a new scheme. "Now y'all lay down and I'll teach you how to spell Granny-style. The way I taught my students." She grinned as if she had a secret.

After she spelled the first word, we were hooked. Choosing a word with multiple syllables, Granny Leola spelled the first syllable and pronounced it, then the second syllable and pronounced it, and then she did something unexpected: she pronounced the first two syllables together. Next, she spelled the third syllable and pronounced it and finally said all three the syllables together.

Most fun were the four-syllable words. The word *invisible* was our favorite. "Do it fast!" we'd beg.

"I-n, in; v-i-s, vis, invis; i, invisi; b-l-e, ble; invisible." She'd grin, knowing she'd nailed the spelling.

The result, especially on long words, was a

melodious chain of letters and sounds. For the rest of the week, we combed our library books to find words we thought would stump her. We never did.

On Friday afternoon, Granny Leola decided to take us on a picnic. We made sandwiches then headed out for Frank's store to buy soda pops and chips. The walk proved to be slow because Dawfie would abruptly stop, standing dead still, mumbling incoherently. Patiently, Granny would wait a few moments, then command, "All right, Dawfie, time to get a move on." Dawfie would start walking again, only to repeat the same action every few hundred years. For two young girls, it was excruciatingly slow.

Sodas and chips finally purchased, we turned to the woods behind the store. "Where are we going?" I asked, surprised to be returning the way we came, except through the woods.

"We're going to the woods. Where else would you have a picnic?" Granny Leola smiled, never breaking her pace.

I looked at my twin and shrugged. To us, a picnic meant a park with picnic tables and, if we were lucky, a set of swings.

After traipsing through deep woods with no clear trail and painstakingly waiting through Dawfie's pauses, we came to a small opening near the creek. Tall pines stood around the opening, having kindly dropped enough pine straw to provide a carpet on the ground.

"This is it. Let's put out the food before the soda pops get hot," Granny said as she grabbed a tablecloth from the bag she carried and spread it on the ground.

Not sure what to do, we plopped down near the edge of the small cloth and waited as Granny Leola set out the food. The intermittent sunrays coming through the trees and the sound of the creek resulted in a pleasant, albeit hot, setting. We ate in silence while Granny Leola told us stories of picnics she took with my grandfather when they first moved to the river. "We'd always see a critter or two, mostly deer but sometimes a shy fox or an armadillo."

Having lived only in cities and towns, bumps rose on my forearms as I hoped no animals would make an appearance today. What did appear was of the two-legged variety. Two young boys walked into the clearing; rifles tucked under their arms. They were as surprised by us as we were by them.

"Howdy, Ms. Leola. Surprised to see you in the woods," said the tall one, who wore a straw cowboy hat with tightly curled sides. The other boy wore a baseball cap proudly stating John Deere Tractors across the front.

"Hello, boys. Hope we didn't scare off anything you were aiming to shoot."

"Reckon not, we ain't far enough in the woods to see anything worth killing." He turned to the silent one and jerked his head away from us. "Best be going if we hope to get a kill afore dark. Y'all enjoy your picnic. Might want to be careful of the redbugs. They like to bed up in pine straw."

I didn't know what redbugs were until later in the evening when the itching started. I found out these tiny red creatures, hardly big enough to see, came with a Texas size itch.

When our father returned the following Saturday morning, my twin and I had attended twelve church services, six dinners on the ground, been chased by a gander, and participated in a picnic with tiny unwelcome quests.

"Son, would you drive me to the dry goods store in Newton? I need some sewing supplies I can't get at Franks' store." Granny Leola barely gave her son time to rest after his long trip.

"Sure, Ma. We'll go right after lunch," Vernon said. "Maybe we'll get Dawfie some ice cream before we come back."

As soon as lunch was over, we piled into Dad's old car to make the hour's drive across the river and into Texas. Dawfie rode in the back seat just behind her brother. Every few miles, she poked him in the back of the head hard enough to bounce his chin forward. "Cream, Crowbaby?" she'd say each time.

Frustrated by the repeated hits on the back of his head, Vernon said forcibly, "Dawfie, if you punch me one more time, I'm turning this car around and you'll get no ice cream."

My twin and I folded our hands over our mouths to suppress giggles. Our bet was he'd keep going, not wanting to disappoint his mother or his sister.

When we arrived at the dry goods store, Granny Leola went straight to the sewing notions, our dad went to hardware, and we girls followed Dawfie as she walked up and down the aisles. Suddenly, she stopped so quickly, we almost bumped into her. Dawfie had planted her feet to the wooden floor in front of a display of small ceramic horses. Her right hand closed into a fist around the largest and most expensive one.

"Wanna," Dawfie said, never taking her eyes off the horse.

"Come on, Dawfie. You can't have that. Let's go find your ma." I tried to persuade her to put the horse back on the shelf, which only made her tighten the grip.

"Wanna." Dawfie turned her back to us.

My twin, always the problem solver, moved in front of Dawfie and tried to pry her fingers off the expensive horse.

Dawfie went from stubborn to a full-blown meltdown in a matter of seconds. She began a warbled scream while hitting the side of her head with the back of her left hand, all the while fiercely holding on to the coveted horse.

Mortified at the behavior and the attention she drew from other shoppers, I wanted to melt through the planks in the floor. In a matter of seconds, Granny Leola moved beside us in the aisle and calmly said, "Doris Lucille, put the horse back on the shelf. There'll be no horse for you today."

Dawfie's screaming and hand flapping stopped as quickly as it started. Slowly, as if a delay might change the outcome, she handed the horse to her mother.

"That's a good daughter," Granny Leola spoke, still in a low, smooth voice. "Let's get my things paid for and we'll go get ice cream." I couldn't get out of the store fast enough, embarrassed by the scene which had taken place in front of a store full of strangers.

Later in the evening, while drying dishes as my

grandmother washed, I asked her, "Granny Leola, doesn't it embarrass you when Dawfie throws a fit in front of other people? All of them were staring and coming from other places to see what was going on."

My grandmother stood silent, her hands in the dishwater. When she spoke, I learned a profound lesson which has stayed with me for a lifetime. "Child, I reckon I don't ever even see anyone looking at us."

In that moment, I knew she unconditionally accepted her daughter just as she was: her daughter first, an adult with a disability second. Years later when I found my own faith, I realized my grandmother's unconditional love came from a far stronger source than just the love of a daughter—it came from the love given to her by the Lord.

I learned something else during that week at Granny's, something with a much more profound effect than the singsong yelling of the preacher's words, something sweet and lasting. I learned of my Granny Leola's love for us and of her strong faith. I couldn't wait for the nightly bedtime routine, which always ended with "Your old granny loves you."

Chapter Thirty-eight

In the late 1980s, a heart condition and weakness brought on by age made it difficult for Granny Leola to care for herself and for Dawfie. After much persuasion with a nursing home director, my father secured a place for both his mother and his sister. They both adjusted well, enjoying the company of the other residents and the knowledge they were safe and cared for. Dawfie was delighted when she discovered the cafeteria served three meals a day. Never once was she late for a meal, generally showing up to be first in line.

On one of my visits to the nursing home, I found Granny Leola brooding alone in her room. "What's wrong? Where's Dawfie?" I asked, concerned to see my usually happy grandmother in obvious displeasure.

"Some man keeps coming to get Dawfie. He says he's testing her. I've tried to tell him she can't read or write, but he insists he can test her anyway." Granny frowned, pulling nervously at the fringe on the homemade crocheted afghan which covered her legs.

"I'm sure it's fine, Granny. Maybe they're just trying to find some activities to interest Dawfie," I said with more confidence than I felt. I cut the visit short and left to find the director.

"Who's testing Dawfie and why?" I asked the busy administrator, who had to be persuaded to see me.

"Oh, it's a man from the State. They're looking at all nursing home residents who are under age sixty and are... well, like Dawfie." She seemed to think this addressed my question and returned to her work.

Even more concerned now, I returned home to search for the reasons for this testing. What I found alarmed me. The State of Louisiana had diagnosticians moving throughout the state testing all cognitively deficient residents in nursing homes who presented no medical need to be there. Their goal, I finally discovered, was to remove these individuals to a different setting such as a group home or a residential home.

A family meeting followed at which my father, sisters, and I discussed our options to prevent the State from taking Dawfie away from her mother, an outcome we knew would be unbelievably difficult for both of them. The greatest problem we faced turned out to be that Granny Leola had never gone before a judge to have Dawfie declared as incompetent. Unless Dawfie's mother had established full guardianship of her daughter, the State regarded Dawfie as an adult. Due to her cognitive capacity, any decisions about her future would be solely the responsibility of the State of Louisiana.

When we discussed the possibility of pursuing guardianship, Granny Leola flatly refused. "I don't need any judge to declare Dawfie as my daughter. I already know that!"

Panicked, we knew we had to do something else. I wrote a letter to the State asking for copies of all testing results. I wrote it from Dawfie and had her sign it with an X. This gave us an idea of what type of setting they might decide as appropriate for Dawfie. Two of my sisters and I held degrees in special education, so we could easily understand the testing results. It didn't surprise any of us when Dawfie's evaluation revealed autism with savant-like tendencies. At the age of fifty-seven, Dawfie finally had a concrete diagnosis of her disability.

After several phone calls, I discovered that a meeting to discuss the evaluation results and make a decision for placement would happen within a few days. Family members quickly rallied with plans to attend the meeting. After the long trip from the Texas coast, we arrived at the nursing home shortly before the meeting time.

Surprised to see all of us and even more surprised when I asked for a wheelchair for Granny Leola so she could attend, Mrs. McNair, the director, stammered, "Oh, no, I don't think they expect anyone at the meeting except Dawfie." She smiled, assuming the family members standing before her would step down. Our feet were glued to the floor, silently communicating our determination to attend the meeting. Defeated, she turned to her secretary with instructions to place more chairs in the meeting room.

Still concerned about the outcome of the meeting, I left the room to make one last phone call to the State of Louisiana Director of Social Services. Talking my way through a host of receptionists and secretaries, I finally had the director on the phone. Our call was short. I admitted we were aware of the lack of input we had in the State's decision about Dawfie but went on to share something I had thought of only recently.

"Mrs. Guidry, I realize there is little we can do to change the State's decision to move my aunt to a different setting. However, please be advised that on the day the State comes to remove her from this facility, our family will make sure every large newspaper and television station in the state will be invited to make public your agency's action to remove a 57-year-old disabled daughter from her 82-year-old mother." I held my breath, hoping for a good outcome.

Finally, Mrs. Guidry spoke. "My field agent is already en route to the facility. When he arrives, please tell him I've requested he only review the testing results today. The State will look further into the matter of placement at another time."

It wasn't a clear answer, but I knew now wasn't the time to press more. "Thank you. I'll let him know we spoke."

When we entered the meeting room, a very surprised young social worker began to protest about our presence. "This is a private meeting for our client only."

"Dawfie invited us to this meeting," I interrupted. "Right, Dawfie?" I held my breath hoping for her customary "Uh huh" to this question. She didn't disappoint me.

At the end of the meeting, after reviewing the testing, the social worker preceded to tell Dawfie the kind of facility the State would move her to. At this point, my father couldn't hold his frustration any longer and started to speak.

Not wanting harmful words to be said which might strengthen the State's case, I interrupted. "Excuse me, sir, I've just been on the phone with the State Director of Social Services. Mrs. Guidry asked me to relay her wishes for you not to make an official decision about the placement of my aunt today."

Sputtering, the red-faced young man had difficulty getting his next words out. "You—you spoke to my boss?"

Six weeks later, Dawfie received a letter from the State of Louisiana saying the nursing facility at which she currently resided would remain her home. I thought again of the story told by Granny Leola when she threatened to call the newspaper when she took Dawfie out of the Charity Hospital in New Orleans. I said a silent prayer thanking God for the stories Granny Leola passed on in those late-night reminisces before the fire.

Chapter Thirty-nine

The call came from my mother. "If you girls want to see your Granny Leola alive one more time, y'all better get on over to Louisiana." More phone calls followed as we four sisters, all in different parts of Texas, made plans to meet and drive over to see our granny.

The drive proved to be a distraction from the reason for the journey, full of sister talk, sharing and banter. One of my sisters brought her young daughter, who reveled in the attention of her three aunts. But soon we arrived at the nursing home, where sight of the typical one-story building reminded us of our mission.

My nose wrinkled the moment we opened the door, assaulted by the stench—a poor attempt at using antiseptic to cover the reek of urine. Residents relaxed on the lobby furniture while others sat in wheelchairs in the hallway. Some acknowledged us with a smile but others looked ahead with a vacant stare, as if their minds had decided to leave before their body did.

An attendant led us to Granny Leola and Dawfie's room. What we found stunned me like nothing I've ever witnessed before. Granny Leola lay in a fetal position in her bed, small and emancipated from age and the coming of imminent death. Yet, in a loud, clear voice, three words flowed from her mouth over and over: "Come, sweet Jesus."

My eyes filled with tears as I gazed at the person in my life whose unconditional love and faith had woven its way deep into my soul, becoming a strong impetus for my own seeking of a relationship with God. During our short stay, she never stopped saying "Come, sweet Jesus." According to the attendant, she had been repeating this for the last two days.

After visiting with Dawfie from the rockers in the front lobby, we retraced our trip back home, each glad we had made the effort to see our grandmother at the end of her life. Granny Leola died two days later.

Her funeral, like all the funerals in my family, was long and loud. Stories mixed with tears and laughter filled the few days preceding her service. At the start of her service, I sat with the rest of the family on the front pew of the church. My fourteen-year-old son squirmed next to his dad looking at the flowers banked on each side of the casket.

One spray of flowers in particular caught his attention. Made of white flowers with pink ribbons, it had a small pink toy phone attached to it. A ribbon lay across the flowers with gold letters which boldly stated, ***Jesus Called.***

My son leaned to his father and whispered,

"Dad, don't you think Granny Leola should have let the answering machine get that call?"

We burst into giggles, trying to camouflage them as sobs by covering our mouths with tissues. Thank God for laughter; it soothed my hurting heart to think of how Granny Leola would have laughed at her great-grandson's statement.

Six months after Leola's death, my father received a call that Dawfie was ill. He left immediately, arriving at the nursing home to find an attendant trying to persuade Dawfie to get on an examination table for the doctor. She was highly agitated, not willing to comply.

Dad quietly asked her to lie down on the table. "For Crowbaby," he said. She settled down immediately and did as her brother asked. Before the doctor could examine her, she looked at her brother and said in a clear voice, "Crowbaby, go see Ma, heaven." Her breathing slowed dramatically and she passed a short time later.

Dawfie's funeral proved so similar to Granny Leola's it could have been a video rewound and played again. Both had the same preacher with very similar words. Both had the song "Sweet By and By" and both caskets were carried to the cemetery next to the church for burial. Dawfie now lay next to Granny Leola in the community which had been their home for six decades.

After the service, I traveled alone to the river road. I needed to see Granny's home place once more. Beside my car, I took in the spot where my grandmother's house once stood, now torn down for lack of care.

However, the bushes still remained. My sight moved from the bridal's wreath from which she occasionally broke a switch to correct one of the children, to the honeysuckle by the back door whose fragrance had welcomed her there as a new bride, and last, to the large hydrangea bushes planted in a circle where my twin and I bathed in a large tub during revival week. All of them the only evidence of a lifetime spent.

Other memories flowed through my mind, like fall leaves floating down a creek. I spent time with each one, examining, recalling, gleaning every small bit before letting it float way. I turned then to the majestic pines across from the road. They still stood tall and sentry-like as if protecting all who travel the river road. Once again, I searched for the reason Dawfie spent so many hours watching the trees from her place on the porch.

A sudden wind rose up and sent the tops of the trees into motion, swaying back and forth as if to music. As suddenly as the wind had come, understanding came. Just like these century-old trees, Leola and Dawfie bent but never broke, regardless of how hard the winds of life blew.

Getting back in my car, I left the river road filled with gratitude for these two amazing women and all they had taught me: how to love, how to live a life of faith, and how to be resilient when life inevitably becomes difficult.

On the trip back to Texas, the words "By and by, I reckon" looped over and over in my mind, marking the miles between my life and the river road.

The End

Discussion Questions

1. Which scene in this story stuck in your head the most?

2. What aspects of the author's story could you most relate to?

3. Were there gaps you wish the author had filled in?

4. Are there characters in the book whose perspective you wanted? Who in this book would you most like to meet? What would you ask or say to him or her?

5. What message/theme do you think the author is trying to make?

6. What was your favorite passage or quote in this book?

7. Does the title *By and By, I Reckon* work for this book?

8. What did you think of the author's writing style? Do the stories about the granddaughter work?

9. How did you feel about the ending?

10. How did you feel when Leola sent Dawfie to the hospital in New Orleans?

11. Can you identify with the loneliness Leola felt living on the river road for so many years?

12. In what ways do you see Leola's character grow in this story?

13. John Thomas and Leola were very much in love even though they seemed very different. What examples of this are present in the book?

14. Why do you think John Thomas turned away from Leola after the death of their second baby?

15. How much control did characters have over their own destiny?

16. Discuss the relationship between characters and setting. How does the physical environment reflect the character's conflicts or attitudes?

Conversation with the Author

What prompted you to write this story about your family? Some stories deserve to be told. I thought this one of those stories—a tale of two women, one with autism, the other determined to face life as it was handed to her with courage and faith. The seed was planted by another memoir I'd read about a similar setting and all through my reading, I imagined telling my story. Once the seed was planted, I just had to do the watering.

How did your relationship with your grandmother and Dawfie shape your life? Well, on the practical side, my grandmother's stories about teaching and growing up with an aunt with autism led to me to pursue a teaching degree specializing in special education. More importantly, knowing my grandmother to never waver from her faith, even in the presence of great loss and hardship, became the catalyst that prompted me to seek faith in my life.

Much of this story is about poverty and you share stories about the poverty you grew up in. Did living in poverty influence your life? It had a huge influence. I managed to go to college and convinced my twin sister to go with me. This encouraged our two younger sisters to go. We were the first to go to college on both sides of our family. Getting a degree broke the cycle of poverty. Later in my career, I was blessed to have the opportunity to become a poverty trainer to help teachers understand how to work with children and parents from poverty.

What is your favorite part in the book? Oh, there are so many. The story of Granny Leola storming Charity Hospital in New Orleans is a favorite because I see so much of me in this story...being strong when strength is needed.

Did you struggle to keep the story true to the actual events? Certainly. I think all writers of a memoir would agree it may be the most difficult part of this genre. I did my research and talked with as many family members as possible to validate my memories. Still, to move the story forward, there are times when I had to "fill in the blanks."

Why did you choose to put your own stories interspersed throughout the book? It certainly didn't start out as intentional. Originally, I had intended to include my story at the beginning of the book. But as I moved the story forward, I realized that many events in my life actually mirrored events in my grandmother's life. My stories seemed to naturally fit into parts of the book. I didn't know I was writing a parallel memoir until someone told me.

A memoir always has a theme, a lesson to be learned. What do you want readers to take with them from this story? Resilience to circumstances and reliance on faith. These two attributes carried my grandmother through the tough times. I'm so thankful to have this example from her life.

Why did you choose this title? I grew up hearing my grandmother and other relatives use this phrase. While writing this story, I researched the phrase and found it is an old English phrase meaning "after a while" or "when it's meant to be." It seems to fit the many circumstances in Leola's life when family members left, and she didn't know when they'd be back.

Do you have any writing quirks? Yes, Bit-o-Honey candies. I treat myself to one when I'm pleased with my writing and, unfortunately, when I'm frustrated with my writing.

What were the key challenges you faced when writing this book? There are always many challenges when writing a memoir. But I think the greatest challenge was staying true to the facts as I knew them. And laying off the Bit-O-Honey candy!

What is one writer's book you use to help you build your craft? The Emotion Thesaurus. It helps me show a character's emotion instead of telling it.

What would you say to others who feel they have

a family story to share? Go for it. There are so many stories out there which represent the fabric of who we are in this country—families who immigrated, families faced with great difficulties, families broken apart and reunited. All of these stories have value to a reader.

Photos:

Below: Leola's teaching certificate

Right, top: Stringtown School, where Leola taught

Right, below: John Thomas and Leola's wedding photo

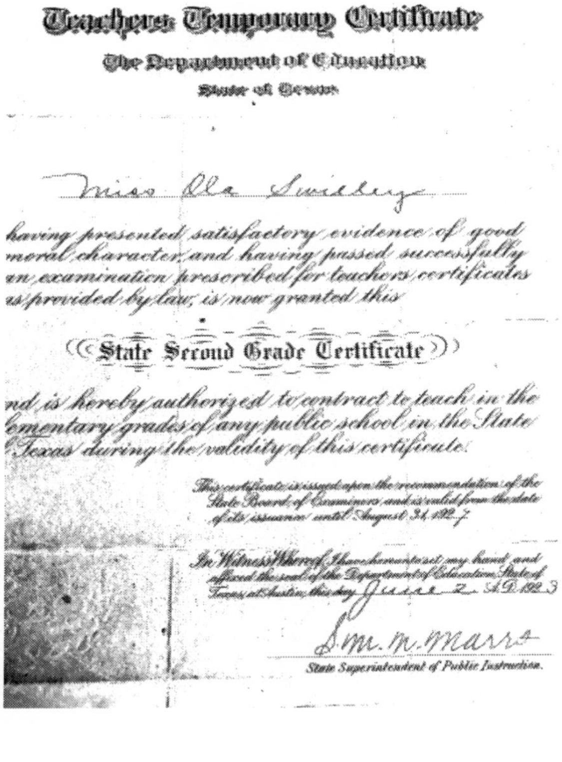

Teachers Temporary Certificate

The Department of Education

State of Texas

Miss Ola Swilley

having presented satisfactory evidence of good moral character, and having passed successfully an examination prescribed for teachers certificates as provided by law, is now granted this

State Second Grade Certificate

and is hereby authorized to contract to teach in the elementary grades of any public school in the State of Texas during the validity of this certificate.

This certificate is issued upon the recommendation of the State Board of Examiners and is valid from the date of its issuance until August 31, 1927

In Witness Whereof I have hereunto set my hand and affixed the seal of the Department of Education, State of Texas, at Austin, this day June 2 A.D. 1923

S. M. N. Marrs

State Superintendent of Public Instruction.

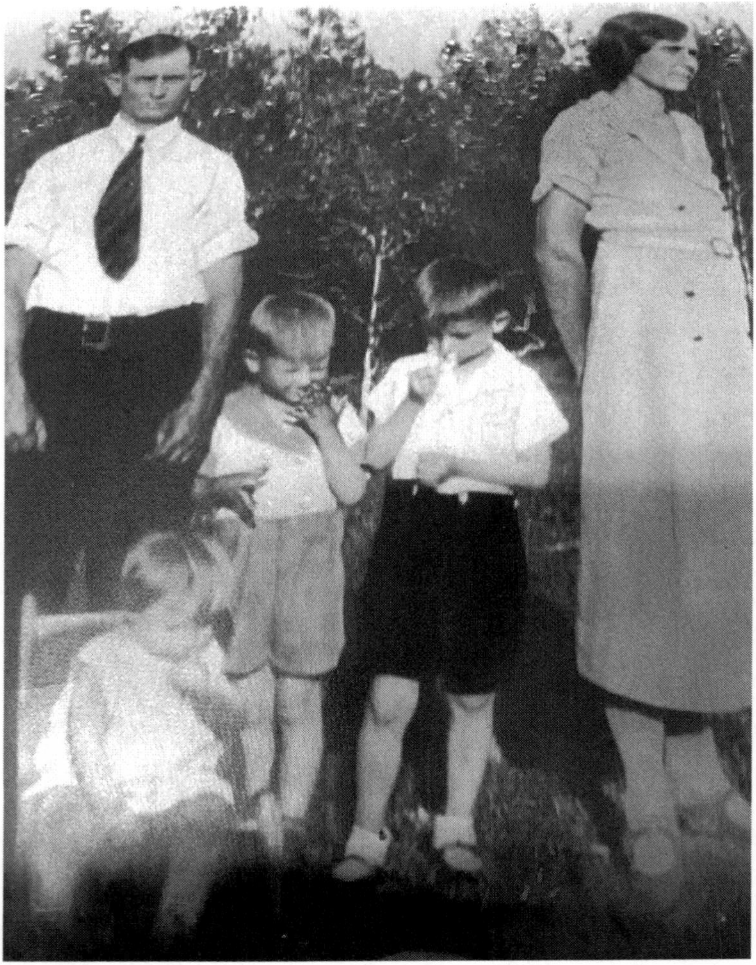

Above: John Thomas, Doris (Dawfie), Vernon (Crowbaby), Wilburn (Teen), and Leola about 1935

Right, top: Charity Hospital in New Orleans, where Dawfie was taken as a young girl for "treatment"

Right, below: Dawfie as a teenager

Charity Hospital. New Orleans, La.

Above: Leola and Dawfie one Easter Sunday

Right: Leola's granddaughter, Brenda O'Bannion

About the Author

Brenda O'Bannion is an author and a retired teacher. Her first book, *Crowbaby and Dawfie,* is a moving book about an autistic child. *Patchwork Annie* uses wordplay to spin a delightful story with a surprise twist at the end. Released in 2019, *What's Up, Cody?* is a children's chapter book about bullying. *By and By, I Reckon* is her first adult novel.

Brenda is a member of the American Christian Fiction Writers and the Water Oak Writing Group. She currently lives with her husband in Georgetown, Texas where she enjoys her book club friends, mentoring moms with school-age children, and teaching in Sunday School. Visit Brenda's website at www.riverroadbooks.com.

Made in the USA
Columbia, SC
03 November 2020

23862743R00167